# BODYWORK

## CAREERS IN MASSAGE THERAPY

by Kayse Gehret

Published by Soulstice Media

Body/Work: Careers in Massage Therapy
By Kayse Gehret

Book Cover and Design: Designarchy

Services for our Readers:
Special rates are available for massage therapy schools, colleges, bookstores and wholesale purchasing.

Contact us:
Soulstice Media
512 Johnson Street Suite A
Sausalito, CA 94965
1.888.988.SOUL

Published by: Soulstice Media

Printed in the United States of America.

ISBN 13: 978-0-615-33076-1
Library of Congress Control Number: 2009911616

# ACKNOWLEDGEMENTS

First and foremost, I'd like to thank my mom and sister for being the wonderful human beings they are. I am lucky to be related to them. Thanks to my mom, Susan, for her caring, nurturing and unlimited patience in listening to my 'latest new idea' over the years. (And then for her unconditional love and support when I actually go and do them.) Thanks to my sister, Annik, for her wit, humor, and being a constant bright light for me and everyone who knows her.

To my friends in the industry…I'd like to thank Leslie Z. Hollingsworth, proprietor of San Francisco Massage Supply, for her excellent editing skills, feedback and inspiration. To Deidre Neal, for her profound talent, friendship and comic relief. To my Reiki teachers, Hillary King Flye and Christopher Campbell, for passing on this magical art. To Joanne Carr, for her compassion and pure heart. A big thanks to the all-star staff at the Mandarin Oriental and Le Meridien hotels in San Francisco, for being immensely supportive of my practice and all-around class acts.

Thanks to the Esalen Institute, the University of California-Santa Cruz, and my many mentors and teachers for supporting, promoting, and inspiring "alternative" healing and learning. Thanks too, to you readers: the students, the curious, and the seasoned professionals always striving to learn more about massage and become the best practitioners you can be. You are the force that shapes this field and makes it so fantastic to be part of.

Jennifer Lynne, author and entrepreneur, provided invaluable advice and helped minimize the number of things I screwed up in the making of this book. Thanks to Tania Kac at Designarchy, for her extraordinary editorial and design work, Sasha Gulish for her amazing photography, and Roanna Biedenweg, ace accountant and gracious advisor.

Finally, this book is dedicated to the many clients I have been honored to know over the course of my career in massage therapy and healing work. Many of you have become cherished friends, and it has been a neverending gift to work with you. You've certainly kept things interesting.

# TABLE OF CONTENTS

# CHAPTER 1

## MASSAGE THERAPY AS A CAREER: THE PRESENT & FUTURE

The ancient art and science of healing touch, popularly known as massage therapy, is re-emerging into the modern consciousness in an amazing way. Over the last decade the profession has grown by leaps and bounds, with day spas, clinics and franchises opening around the world. Millions of people have experienced having at least one massage, and every day more people are becoming aware of massage therapy as a valuable, preventative health practice. Massages aren't just for luxury anymore!

It is estimated there are over 300,000 massage students and therapists in the United States today, and that number is growing yearly. The explosive growth of the industry is a welcome sign as the public becomes more aware of the many benefits of massage and fuels its growth with demand for spas and healing services. With more and more therapists entering the field, it is all the more crucial that you differentiate yourself with your skills and business practices.

The intention of this book is to serve as your companion and guide as you embark on the path of a massage therapist, healer and business person. Inside, you will find plenty of business basics, nuts and bolts, and step-by-step marketing advice. You will also find the insider tips, professional advice and mistake-prevention hints that one could normally only learn through experience. Whether you are just considering a career in massage therapy, currently in massage school or already working in the field, this book will provide you with valuable assistance in getting you certified, building a successful practice and creating a fulfilling career.

## Why Massage?

If you are brand new to the world of massage, welcome! You will no doubt immediately discover a common reason why massage therapy is so popular: it feels great! Bodywork relieves muscular tension, strengthens the immune system, promotes healing and detoxification, improves circulation, lowers stress, offers emotional reassurance, balances energy, improves appearance and increases the healthy functioning of the skin. Regular massage therapy improves athletic performance and helps prevent injury and illness by lowering stress and maintaining flexibility. Not too shabby! Let's face it, when we feel good, we look better, we're more productive at work, have more patience, and move through each day with greater ease and grace.

Massage therapy also provides vital, caring human touch, something many of us in this high-tech, fast-paced society could use a lot more of. It gives many people a refuge from the stresses of daily life, a consistent hour of peace and sanctuary. Regular massage can provide the intimate connection and depth of conversation that so often seems lacking in modern culture. How often in life do we spend time one-on-one with anyone, providing compassionate care and listening? When was the last time someone gave you their absolute, full focus and attention? Massage therapy - with its wealth of benefits - is one of the greatest gifts you can give another person.

Being a massage therapist is one of the most fulfilling professions on the planet, and it has every potential to provide you with a deeply rewarding career. As independent massage practitioners, we often get to set our own hours and schedule, get paid an above-average hourly wage, and have the ability to be our own boss. We can take vacations or time off when we need or want to. And best of all, we have the ability to make an enormous difference in the lives and well-being of our clients. It is a wonderful feeling to know that a client's session with you is often the highlight of their day!

And who doesn't love getting a massage? Massage therapists are universally beloved. As soon as you reveal your profession to a new acquaintance, people often have a hard time containing their interest and enthusiasm. Massages are the number one requested service at spas around the United States, and our health care system is rapidly beginning to recognize massage therapy as a beneficial preventative and rehabilitative health practice. Many health savings plans now include massage therapy in their coverage, as do health insurance programs with a prescription from a doctor.

Massage is a growth field that is showing no signs of slowing down. The U.S. Department of Labor predicts that employment for massage therapists is expected to increase 20% between 2006-2016. As the populous baby boomer generation moves into their fifties and sixties there will be a growing societal emphasis on staving off old age by staying active and engaging in healthy practices such as massage. Our rapidly growing field is poised for even more growth in the years ahead.

The longer you are in the field of massage therapy, the more you will find kindred spirits among your fellow therapists. The colleagues and associates you will meet on your massage journey will be among the most caring, empathetic and, frankly, interesting people around. As a group, we embrace wellness, healing and individuality, honoring the spirit and interconnectedness of us all. If you are seeking a career filled with meaning, one where you can make a difference every day, look no further. Massage promises that and much, much more.

I will let you in on a little secret, here. In time, massage will feel as good to give as it does to receive. The practice of focusing intently, letting go of the 'mind,' and channeling compassion and caring is as beneficial to the giver as it is to the recipient. The exchange of energy and kindness is healing for both client and therapist. I've certainly ended work days feeling physically exhausted, sore or a little worn out, especially at the outset of my practice. But, I've always ended those same days feeling that my heart is more open, more balanced and emotionally uplifted.

On the other hand, being a massage therapist has its challenges as well. We are reliant on our physical body, especially our hands and arms. Make no mistake, massage therapy is manual labor! Therefore, it is imperative that we keep our energy up by eating healthfully and getting sufficient sleep, exercise and time off to allow our bodies to recover. We also must be aware of our tendency to take on other people's energy and stress. The same qualities that make us excellent practitioners (intuition, openness, empathy) also put us at some risk of transference, especially when just starting out in our practice. (More about transference and tips on how to limit this occurrence will be covered in Chapter 10.)

As an independent practitioner, you will need to learn some basic business and marketing skills to build your client base into a thriving practice. If you are accustomed to a job where you receive benefits and a predictable, consistent paycheck, being accountable for these things on your own may take some getting used to. As an independent massage therapist you will also be responsible for self-employment taxes, requiring you to keep careful records and receipts for tax purposes.

Despite its massive growth in popularity, massage is still looked at by some as a luxury. Therefore, when the economy dips and people are looking to cut back on their spending, their massages are often one of the first things to go. It is extremely important to budget, plan and save for those stretches in the future when you might have to rely on your savings for a period of time.

## Is Massage Therapy the Right Career For You?

Massage therapists come in all shapes, sizes and motivations, but across the board most therapists will tell you they do this work because they love helping people. Whether it is alleviating someone's physical pain, helping a client recover emotionally from a break up, or providing solace from a stressful career, massage therapists are givers and healers.

Contemplating your motivation when you are starting out will help you choose which type of massage to study, your first place of employment, where to advertise your practice, and much more. Some of you may be coming from a job or career that could not be more different from massage therapy; you may have no idea what to expect. One of the goals of this book is to give you a realistic picture of what it means to be a professional massage therapist and outline the opportunities that will be available to you. With its myriad paths and possibilities, you may wish to think of massage less like a job and more like an unfolding adventure!

Spend some time alone imagining and envisioning your ideal career. What does the setting look like? Who are you working with? What is your typical client's lifestyle like? Do you love sports and working with athletes? Do you gravitate toward spas and luxury services? Does the idea of working on specific injuries or physical problems sound appealing? Are you results-oriented? Nurturing? A fitness buff? The possibilities are infinite.

Speak with family and friends who know you well and get their thoughts. Visit spas, fitness centers and massage clinics in your area and ask questions. Find a massage therapist you admire and ask them if they'd be willing to talk with you. Time spent researching your options is time well spent; intention is an amazingly powerful helpmate to manifesting your reality!

> *If a spa owner or massage therapist takes time to answer your questions or give advice, don't forget to thank them, preferably with a hand-written thank you note. They will really appreciate and remember you for it!

That said, keep an open mind as to where your practice might take you. The universe has its own sort of wisdom, and it isn't always in keeping with our human logic nor our idea of what should happen next. How will you figure this out? Simply by the type of experiences that will suddenly start happening! Once you enter the world of massage, you will quickly learn that people come to massage therapy for all sorts of reasons (see Chapter 10 for more on this subject), not simply because they strained their back or have a sore knee. The point of this story is, keep an open mind! Try not to focus exclusively on one "area" of massage and take opportunities to expose yourself to other forms of healing and bodywork.

Finally, get lots of massage! Try as many different massage modalities as you can. Explore different spas and wellness centers. Receive massages from as many bodywork practitioners as you can. Take along a small notebook and after your visit jot down notes, likes, dislikes and general thoughts that you can look back on later.

## Traits of Successful Therapists

Creating a thriving massage therapy practice is equal parts skill, persistence, heart and personality. There are some fabulous technically skilled practitioners out there who are great with a rotator cuff but not-so-great with the human it belongs to. You may succeed to a degree with skill alone, but your practice will be self-limiting if you don't cultivate the necessary personal skills. Likewise, a therapist may have a terrific personality, but if they don't continue to learn and grow in their skills they will limit their practice, too. It's vitally important to continually expand upon our strengths and work on our weaknesses, both as people and practitioners.

The most successful massage therapists I have come across artfully blend the following traits:

Professionalism – Successful therapists treat their practice, their customers and themselves as professionals. They are reliable, responsive, punctual and hold themselves to a stellar professional standard.

Enthusiasm – Successful therapists are very "into" what they do. They care about their clients, they love giving massages, and it shows in their day to day work. Likewise, they enjoy reading about bodywork, attending massage workshops and continuing to grow in their practices.

Service-oriented and Caring – Therapists tend to be compassionate "people-persons."

Strong Communication Skills – Successful therapists are clear, direct, warm and non-judgmental in their communications. Massage therapy is a very personal, intimate profession that requires trust on the part of the client for them to fully relax and enjoy the maximum benefits of their sessions. Great therapists consistently communicate trust and integrity through both their words and actions.

Persistence - Good things take time! Once you enter the field, keep at it and give yourself time to succeed. As with most things in life, it takes time to become a confident massage professional. Be kind and patient with yourself, and allow yourself time to grow into your new role. Many therapists give up on their practice too soon. Building a solid client base requires a steady stream of consistent effort and dedication over time. Successful therapists learn to work productively through setbacks, keeping in mind that we often experience our greatest frustrations just before making significant breakthroughs.

Personal Growth - Finally, practice heart-opening exercises and seek out growth experiences for yourself. The more you can cultivate kindness and openness in your own heart, the more you will be able to provide that to your clients. Meditation, yoga, laughter, loving and being loved will keep your heart open, strong and overflowing with energy. Successful therapists are constantly learning and growing while striving for balance in their personal and professional lives.

# CHAPTER 2

## TYPES OF MASSAGE

Masseuse... masseur... bodyworker... therapist. These are just a few of the terms you may come to be called. Confusing? When it comes to the types of massage out there, the choices are even greater!

Many massage schools specialize in training for certain massage modalities, so it's a good idea to familiarize yourself with the many types and styles of massage as you research various schools and programs. The variety and modalities of massage and bodywork are growing all the time, but here is a basic "primer" on the most common forms.

### Swedish:

Swedish massage is characterized by long effleurage (flowing) strokes of varying speeds combined with kneading, stretching and pressure from the practitioner's hands, knuckles, and forearms. The pressure may vary from light to firm, but always includes sweeping circulatory strokes. Swedish massage can be relaxing, invigorating or both! It is the most common and requested type of massage in the United States, and considered the "default" or basic massage offered at most spas and resorts.

### Deep Tissue:

Deep tissue massage is a firm to deep style of bodywork that works very slowly to get into the fascia, muscle and connective tissue to break up adhesions. An extremely popular form of massage - especially among stressed and active clients - it unwinds the deep muscle layers (typically over a few to many sessions depending on the state of the client's body and stress level.)

### Sports:

Sports massage is for recreational and professional athletes as well as active clients. This style of massage varies with the type of sport or exercise done by the client, as well as their training and fitness goals. Instruction in sports massage will offer very specific knowledge about the anatomy and musculature as well as how to approach massage during, before and after competitive events. Sports massage also

tends to include a good deal of stretching and resistance work, and
the massage strokes are typically performed at a higher rate than other
massage styles, giving it an energizing quality. In this style of massage,
the emphasis is usually on preventing injury and improving performance
rather than relaxation.

## Pre-Natal/Pregnancy/Perinatal:

This specialized massage modality is tailored specifically to pregnant
clients and/or the time before or following childbirth. Therapists who
practice this type of work are trained to work with the issues common
in pregnancy, such as hip and lower back soreness, tight shoulders and
sciatica. There are certain points on the lower body that are contraindicated
for pregnant clients because they are thought to bring the energy
downward (ideal during childbirth, but not before the baby is ready!) Prenatal massage therapy training will include a comprehensive education
on points and places to avoid while massaging a pregnant client. Special
cushions are available for pregnant clients that can help them lie more
comfortably on the massage table, especially welcome in the last trimester!

## Infant Massage:

Delicate massage can be performed upon newborns and infants to aid in
their healthy development. Studies have shown that regular, nurturing
touch is vital for young children. Many practitioners of infant massage
also hold seminars or classes to teach parents the techniques so they may
practice and bond with their babies through massage at home.

## Shiatsu:

Shiatsu is an Asian (Japanese) style of massage that utilizes acupressure
and reflex points along the body's meridians. Shiatsu is typically
performed while the client wears loosely fitting clothes. The practitioner
primarily uses his/her thumbs, forearms and elbows to apply rhythmic,
firm and focused pressure across the body. This energetic modality is an
excellent choice for modest clients who are new to massage and would
prefer to keep their clothing on.

## Aromatherapy:

This style of healing massage incorporates scented plant oils or blends
(known as essential oils) that possess beneficial properties. A few drops
of essential oils are typically placed in the carrier, or primary, massage
oil or lotion rather than being placed directly onto the skin. Pure
essential oils are very powerful and a little bit goes a long way. Oils can
be relaxing, energizing, or balancing, and are particularly well-suited for
stress reduction and relaxation massage.

## Ayurvedic Massage:

Ayurveda is a traditional Indian form of medicine that incorporates massage, herbs and dietary regimens as well as yoga. Ayurvedic massage addresses the marma points ("vital body parts" where bones, muscles, joints and arteries come together; similar to trigger points), nadis (nerve points), and chakras (energy centers.) Common styles of ayurvedic massage performed in the West are Abhyanga and Shirodhara.

## Reflexology:

Popularly known as "foot massage," reflexology is the application of firm to deep pressure to the reflex points on the feet, hands or ears (but is most commonly done on the feet.) Reflexology is based on the principle that the entire body and organs are reflected in these reflex points, making it possible to address imbalances throughout the body solely through the feet. This is an especially wonderful treatment for high heel-wearers, individuals who stand on their feet all day, and extremely modest people who are uncomfortable with being touched in a traditional massage.

## Rolfing/Orthopedic/Medical/Structural Massage:

These extremely deep styles of bodywork delve into the deep tissues and realign the body at a structural level. Clients who receive these types of massage have ideally experienced regular treatments and have bodies that are accustomed to deep pressure. These styles of bodywork are often accompanied by physical therapy, rehabilitation, and sports medicine or chiropractic treatments.

## Hot Stone:

Hot stone massage incorporates the use of warm, smooth stones in place of the practitioner's hands alone. Heated stones are especially wonderful to use on the large, heavy muscles of the back and shoulders. You may purchase special heaters to keep the rocks warmed in proximity to your table, or you can use a crock pot. Hot Stone massages are typically 1.25 to 1.5 hours in length.

## Esalen:

Esalen massage is based on a style of massage founded and developed at the Esalen Institute in Big Sur, California. While the technique of an Esalen massage will vary according with its practitioner, the common characteristic among all is the flowing, continuous strokes of the massage, emphasizing a constant connection to the client. This nurturing style of bodywork is typically performed more slowly than other modalities, therefore sessions are usually ninety minutes or more in length.

## Thai Massage:

Also known as "passive yoga," Thai massage is commonly performed on a floor mat with the client dressed in loose, comfortable clothing. Similar to Shiatsu, this modality aligns the body's energy by applying firm pressure to specific meridians and points while the therapist moves the client into a variety of postures and stretches. Thai massage is a very active, energizing style of bodywork that is excellent for improved flexibility and range of motion. A typical Thai massage session is 1.5 to 2 hours in length.

## Cranio-Sacral:

Cranio-sacral is a very gentle form of bodywork that involves the therapist manipulating the craniosacral system. By gently working with the spine, neck and cranial bones, the restrictions of nerve passages are said to be eased, the movement of cerebrospinal fluid through the spinal cord optimized, and misaligned bones restored to their proper position. Craniosacral therapy can be very effective in reducing stress, neck and back pain, headaches, TMJ and for chronic pain conditions such as fibromyalgia.

## Lomi Lomi:

Lomi Lomi is the traditional massage of Hawaii, characterized by rhythmic, sweeping strokes. It incorporates the use of the practitioner's hands, fingers, forearms, knuckles, elbows and occasionally, the feet. A Lomi lomi practice often emphasizes the role of prayer and intention - the "Spirit of Aloha" - as a companion to harmony and healing.

## Lymphatic Massage:

Also known as *lymphatic drainage*, lymphatic massage is a very gentle process that enhances the natural circulation of lymph through the body, assisting in detoxification and strengthening the immune system. It is accomplished by working with the lymphatic system, which is largely clustered in the head, face, upper torso and groin regions. Lymphatic massage employs a very light touch, is extremely relaxing and is thought to be especially beneficial for sinus conditions, cleansing, and clients concerned with wrinkles and aging.

## Myofascial Release:

Using the hands or rolling instruments, the myofascial therapist uses compression and stretching to release adhesions in the connections between the fascia and muscles. This style of bodywork can be extremely light or very deep, depending on the area being treated.

## Tui Na:

A Chinese style of massage, often vigorous and energizing, that it is characterized by pulling, pinching, and kneading.

## Watsu:

Watsu is a Shiatsu-like style of massage performed with both the client and practitioner immersed in a pool of warm water. Typically, the pool is shallow enough for the therapist to stand comfortably, but deep enough for the client to feel as if they are floating when held. The water allows the client to feel buoyant and weightless as pressure is applied to pressure points and meridians. Gentle holds and stretches are performed, allowing the joints to open and relax.

## Energy Work:

There are countless forms of Energy Work, including Reiki, Polarity, Healing Touch, and many more. Most energetic therapies are practiced with the practitioner laying their hands upon the client and holding certain positions while the energy flows out or through the therapist's hands and client's body. Energy work is a subtle, gentle form of healing bodywork that opens, clears and balances the energetic pathways and chakras in the body. Energy work is generally safe for all clients, especially those whose physical limitations or illnesses are contraindicated for regular massage therapies.

## Animal Massage:

Animals love therapeutic touch as much as humans do! Animal Massage adapts and incorporates massage techniques so they may be performed on animals, most commonly dogs, cats or horses (called Equine Massage.)

# CHAPTER 3

## YOUR MASSAGE EDUCATION

Your massage education is likely to be a large investment of your time and money, so it's worth committing some time to research your options well. If you're familiar with using the internet, spend some time using search engines to explore the schools in your area. As of 2004, there were over eight hundred massage schools in the United States alone, giving you many options to explore!

Key Questions to Address When Researching Massage Programs:
  a.  How long is the program (number of hours) for certification?
  b.  What modalities are covered by the certification program? (Basic techniques? Eastern modalities?)
  c.  Will the program prepare you for the National Certification Exam (NCBTMB)?
  d.  Does the program offer extensive anatomy & physiology coursework?
  e.  Is the faculty established, with long-term instructors?
  f.  How long has the school been in operation?
  g.  What is the average class size?

Living at home while attending massage school is the most cost-effective way to go, but may not always be possible. If you are able, it is well worth taking a day to visit schools in person, meet some of the staff and students and possibly even sit in on a class or two. Many schools offer "open house" days or evenings, special events designed to welcome new and prospective students and introduce them to their program. If a school is nearby, you may wish to enroll in a single class or workshop before committing to a long certification program.

You can locate massage schools in your area by asking practicing therapists where they went to school and obtained their certification. You can also find lists of programs online, in the Massage Therapy Journal, and through advertisements in various massage magazines. Professional massage associations such as the AMTA, ABMP and IMA have valuable educational information and school listings on their websites. (You can find more on these associations and their contact information in Chapter 4.)

Some programs offer training strictly in massage and bodywork, while others offer various allied health programs or vocational schools. Some will be more "touchy feely" or esoteric in feel while others will be highly clinical and technical in approach. Schools may incorporate a spiritual aspect while others are completely secular. Other programs will be a mix of all of the above, diverse and dependent upon the personality and perspective of each individual instructor. With the vast and growing number of choices, it is more important than ever to research and visit a school in person so you can be confident it will be a good fit for your goals.

Another advantage to checking out schools in person is so you can see the location and facility with your own eyes, which may or may not be different than the impression given by the school's website or brochures. In person, you can see the quality of the classrooms, the equipment and the supplies provided by the school. Does the school emphasize quality of instruction? Having the best equipment? Does it attract a sizeable and diverse student body through marketing? You can get a better sense of the answers to these questions in person than you ever could at a distance. Remember, when you are looking at massage programs, *people* are the most important attribute of any school. During your visit, focus on getting to know the teachers, the faculty, staff, and current students. They, more than anything else, will give you an excellent sense of a school.

If it's not possible to visit schools in person, don't hesitate to give them a call. Most programs have staff specially assigned to assist and counsel new students; they are a great resource and happy to answer your questions. Request a catalogue and take note of how long the programs are, how many times they are offered throughout the year, and the backgrounds of the instructors. Alumni and current students are often the best source of information and can share details that you won't necessarily find in any catalogue. Ask practitioners in your area where they attended school and if there were any particular classes or instructors they would recommend.

Although a national certification exam has been available since 1992, as of this writing the requirements for massage certification and licensure still vary widely from state to state, and even city to city. If you are contemplating attending massage school in another state, you will want to take special care in researching if your certification will qualify in the state you will be practicing (also known as 'reciprocity.') This is not always the case!

The cost of living also varies greatly from state to state, so be sure to budget living expenses along with your education if you'll be relocating to attend school. Massage schools are typically aware that many students have full-time jobs, families and other responsibilities to consider while they are enrolled. Therefore, many of them offer evening, weekend or intensive programs to accommodate many types of schedules. Check with your potential schools to see if they offer or have access to financial aid, grants, work-study programs or housing resources for students.

An important item to consider when researching schools is if they offer an internship program or partner with other institutions to provide new massage therapists entry level work in the field. Check around to see if they maintain any partnerships or an active job board. Many massage programs require that students complete a certain number of practice hours of supervised massages before they are granted certification. Does your school maintain a clinic program? Offer graduate or continuing education programs? Cultivate alliances with local spas, hospitals or sports medicine organizations? Ask other students or alumni what type of support the school offers graduates entering the work force.

> *Occasionally a massage school may offer discounts on coursework and programs in exchange for pre-payment. These offers can save you a great deal of money, but be sure to review the refund policy. At a minimum, find out if there *is* a refund policy! In a worst case scenario (for example, the school closes halfway through your program) you want to be certain you can get your money back or otherwise complete your certification.

The vast majority of massage therapists look back on their time in massage school very fondly. It is a time of great learning and growth, allows for the creation of deep bonds and friendships, and is typically meaningful and lots of fun. Your massage education is likely to be a time of enormous personal growth, as you will be experiencing a lot of bodywork and healing during classes and practice sessions. Be prepared for some "shifts" to occur in your life, and be aware that changes in you may also impact the people around you. Becoming more in balance and in touch with our truest selves allows us to let go of habits and relationships that no longer serve us or contribute positively to our lives. Change is not always easy or comfortable, but it is a necessary component to a full and evolving existence. If you hold space open for the possibility of shifts and changes, they will come as less of a surprise and more naturally integrate themselves into your life.

# CHAPTER 4

## TIPS FOR THE NEW MASSAGE THERAPIST

It can be a bit of a rude awakening once you leave the nurturing, all-encompassing world of massage school, and the transition back to the "real world" can be a bit jarring. Gone is the schedule, the structure and being surrounded by people who 'get it'; back you go into the unknown, the undecided and perhaps to face some family members who think massage school was a crazy idea in the first place.

It may take you some time to adjust to your new identity as a massage therapist, health practitioner and healer. Your acquaintances, friends and loved ones may also need some encouragement from you before they begin to view you in this new light. (More on "re-branding" yourself in Chapter 8.)

If you are a person who requires structure (and most of us need at least some), you may wish to create a schedule for yourself before you completely transition out of school. This may be as simple as making daily and weekly plans for yourself, or as elaborate as creating massage student groups with regular get-togethers. You may also want to pre-plan workshops in advance; this is a great idea if you are still working full-time at a job unrelated to massage therapy as it will keep you connected to the field going forward. Maintaining some semblance of a schedule and support system will ease the transition between school and your first job in the field. Massage school will provide you with a wonderful foundation, but soon you will find it is just the beginning of your journey. As long as you practice massage, you will continue to learn from colleagues, life experience and, most of all, your clients.

Many consider the practice of massage to be akin to an art or trade. Historically, these professions are learned through mentoring, where a master takes the student under his/her wing and instructs them individually over time. Individuals attain expert status not through a grade or degree but by training supported by their mentor. If this style of learning appeals to you, seek out practitioners that you admire and approach them about forming a teacher-apprentice relationship with you. Not only will you learn better technique and skills, a successful mentor will also teach you a plethora of business skills and lessons on how to balance work and life. If you are fortunate enough to find yourself in one of these relationships, take advantage of this fantastic opportunity for learning.

## Certification and Licensing

There is often some confusion in the massage therapy field between the terms certification and licensure. Once you graduate massage school and complete your required clinic hours, you will typically be granted certification as a *massage therapist* or *massage technician*. In some locations, you will be required to pass an exam before you can receive your certification. Certification is a type of degree or proof that you have achieved a basic level of professional mastery, and typically must be completed before you apply for licensure.

As of this writing, 42 states and Washington D.C. regulate massage therapy or provide a voluntary certification. Since 1992, the NCBTMB (National Certification Board for Therapeutic Massage & Bodywork) has administered an exam for therapists to attain a nationally recognized certification. To obtain this level of certification, therapists must pass the exam, complete 500+ hours of training, attain continuing education credits and adhere to an established code of ethics. A number of states recognize this national certification as their own standard for certification and it may be a prerequisite to licensure in some locations. You can find more information about the exam at www.ncbtmb.org.

Before you can begin to legally practice massage, you will often need to obtain a massage and/or business license within your local community. Unlike certification, a license gives you the legal right to practice massage therapy. As of this writing, licensure still varies from state to state, county to county, and city to city. It is important to research and be fully versed on license requirements before you sign a lease or open an office within a particular city or county.

Once you are certified, check to see if your state has any specific licensing requirements. Your massage school, assuming it is in the same state you will be practicing, should be able to help you with this. Or, you can ask practicing massage therapists in your area.

If you live in an unincorporated area of your county, you may need to obtain a massage and/or business license from the county. You can find out by calling or visiting the county business office.

If you plan to operate your business under a name other than your own, you will likely need to file an assumed name, "doing business as" name (a.k.a. DBA) or fictitious business declaration with the county as well. This would be true if you live anywhere within the county, unincorporated areas or not. For example, the name of my first massage practice was called "Soulstice Massage & Bodywork", not "Kayse Gehret." Since I wasn't using my actual name, I was required to file a DBA with the county and publish the declaration in a local newspaper for a specified length of time. This process may be necessary regardless if you operate as a sole proprietor, partnership or corporation (more on these options will be explored later.) Steps will vary by location, so check with your individual county to learn exactly what is required of you.

## Zoning & Permits

The town or city you will be practicing in usually oversees zoning, parking, business licenses, and any massage business operational or educational requirements. It is important to befriend and be on good terms with the city employees who deal with these issues; they can be of great help if you ever run into a problem. Some jurisdictions will require you to undergo fingerprinting and other documentation, while others still operate under archaic zoning laws that prohibit massage therapy businesses. Yes, it's weird, but be patient as we collectively move our field into the 21st century! Because the regulations can vary so much, it's very important to know what they are before you commit to a particular location. You definitely want to know what they are and have all requirements in place ahead of signing a lease. This way you are able to hit the ground running without procedural delays as soon as you open your doors.

While all this talk of licenses and permits may sound complicated, please don't let it overwhelm or dishearten you. The large majority of therapists will be happy to assist you in learning the ropes; all you need to do is ask for help. Approach licensing and permits with an attitude to do your best to be informed and compliant. Before you know it, the process will be complete and far behind you.

Once you obtain them, keep all of your certificates and licenses in a safe and secure location. It's a great idea to keep these papers, along with insurance and other important business documents, in a small fire-proof safe. (You can find these easily at office supply stores or online.) Once you receive permission from the city or county to do anything, be sure to always get it in writing. I also like to write down the names of any government employees who helped me on any particular issue and the date so that I can refer back and remember them in case an issue arises later.

> *When visiting government offices to obtain information or licensure, dress professionally and present yourself with a friendly attitude. Have patience, and leave enough space in your day to accommodate lines or unforeseen delays. Doing these things can make a big difference in how smoothly and efficiently you receive the results you need. During the course of your licensing process, you may deal with a myriad of city or county employees, government workers, and possibly even the local police department. Look at these interactions as wonderful opportunities to increase the perception of massage therapy in a positive way. You may even get a new client or two out of it!

As you progress through the years as a massage therapist, you will often be required to complete a certain number of Continuing Education Credits (CEUs) each year before you can renew your license. Additionally, many professional massage associations require a specific number of CEUs to maintain your membership. Typically you can acquire these credits by taking a weekend workshop or a few classes. As a new therapist, stay abreast of the requirements so you can plan for these classes in advance and not run out of time at the end of the year.

## So, You're Legal. Now What?!

### PROFESSIONAL ASSOCIATIONS

The crucial time between graduating from massage school and beginning your practice can be nerve-wracking. Keep the momentum going by reading books and magazines on massage as well as giving and receiving plenty of bodywork. Stay in touch with your massage school friends and develop new relationships with established therapists. You may also wish to join a professional massage association at this time. Many therapists are introduced to these associations through the need to obtain liability insurance before they can be hired (most associations include liability insurance as part of their membership) but membership offers many other benefits as well.

Liability insurance policies may include professional liability (malpractice), premises liability (slip and fall coverage), advertising injury, personal injury, rental damage insurance and product liability coverage.

Explore each membership organization, the liability coverage it provides and benefits it offers in order to decide which one is best for you.

The three major professional massage associations are:

**ABMP**
Associated Bodywork & Massage Professionals
25188 Genesee Trail Road Suite 200
Golden, Colorado 80401
www.abmp.org
expectmore@abmp.com
800-458-2267 (telephone)
800-667-8260 (fax)

The Associated Bodywork & Massage Professionals organization offers five different membership levels: student, practitioner, professional, aesthetician, and certified. Student memberships start at $45 per year (without liability insurance) and $65 (with liability insurance.) ABMP membership allows for the inclusion of certain non-massage allied health practices such as aesthetics and energy work; aestheticians joining ASCP (Associated Skin Care Professionals) receive many of the same benefits and coverage of ABMP members. Massage therapists interested in performing skin care, too, can get more information on these memberships ($259 per year) by phoning 1-800-789-0411 or visiting www.ascpskincare.com.

ABMP's liability coverage also covers hot stone massage, cupping (a healing technique) and includes legal defense coverage. It also offers property insurance for $95 per year in the event your table, equipment and supplies are damaged or stolen. You may add your landlord or employer to your policy at no extra cost by making additionally insured endorsements.

Supporting memberships are available for individuals who may not require liability insurance but would like access to the many benefits ABMP offers its members. These benefits include access to group health, disability and life insurance, a members-only credit card, a therapist referral directory (www.massagetherapy.com), and the promotion of International Massage Week held in July of each year. Membership automatically includes its bimonthly magazine (*Massage & Bodywork*), newsletter (*Different Strokes)*, and a magazine for you to distribute to your clients – *Body Sense* – ($1 per copy for members.) Members also receive offers for discounted travel privileges, automobile and home insurance, mobile phone and credit card processing rates, and many other services.

Members can access many of their benefits through the ABMP website. There you will find tools to create your own free website as well as a photo directory from which to pull massage-related images for your own marketing materials. Templates for client newsletters and brochures are provided, as well as a continuing education calendar, a business handbook, massage article database, and an online store. A secondary website, massagetherapy.com, is published to provide educational support and provide a referral resource network.

The ABMP website allows you to enroll in their programs and register online and is available in a Spanish version. It lists massage schools that participate in its Massage School Alliance program and the organization created massageprofessionals.com, a social networking site especially for massage therapists.

### AMTA
American Massage Therapy Association
500 Davis Street, Suite 900
Evanston, Illinois 60201-4695
www.amtamassage.org
info@amtamassage.org
877-905-2700 (telephone)
847-864-5196 (fax)

The American Massage Therapy Association (AMTA) offers several levels of membership: student, associate and professional. In additional to its national membership, it also offers regional membership to chapters within the organization, occasionally charging an additional "chapter fee." Student memberships start at $79 per year, while professional memberships begin at $235 per year. Both include liability insurance coverage. Associate, or supporting, memberships include all the benefits of AMTA membership except liability coverage, and those begin at $99 yearly. You can enroll and register in the AMTA online.

The AMTA offers many continuing education resources, sponsors a national multi-day massage convention each year, maintains active regional chapters around the country, and promotes National Massage Therapy Awareness Week held every October each year. They also offer group health, disability and life insurance, a quarterly magazine (*The Massage Therapy Journal*), and a public directory of its massage therapist members.

The AMTA website maintains a members-only job bank and classified ads, an online store, a massage school directory, and an extensive glossary of massage terms. Members may opt to receive an online newsletter and access the excellent "industry fact sheets," current facts and figures about the massage therapy field. Since its founding, the AMTA has formed a powerful lobbying effort, working toward positive changes through legislation that affects massage therapists. The organization has consistently emphasized research and standardization in the industry. For example, the AMTA played a significant role in the creation of the national certification exam for massage, and it continues to support ongoing scientific research, field studies and lobbies for state and national certification laws. The organization is a strong supporter of volunteerism, and provides smaller membership units within chapters that provide monthly meetings and a strong sense of community.

## IMA

International Massage Association
25 South 4th Street
Warrenton, Virginia 20186
www.imagroup.com
info@imagroupinc.com
540-351-0800 (telephone)
540-351-0816 (fax)

The International Massage Association (IMA) emphasizes accessibility, requiring only 100 hours of education or work as an apprentice to qualify for membership. These "practicing" memberships ($199 per year) also require that you achieve 16 continuing education credits every four years. "Therapist" memberships (also $199 per year) are available for practitioners who have 500+ hours of training and require 16 continuing education credits every two years.

If you plan to do any teaching in the massage field, your practicing or therapist membership will automatically include liability coverage for teaching classes of 1-9 students. To teach larger classes (10-99 students) you can upgrade your membership ($299 per year.) Individuals who would like to receive IMA benefits but don't require liability insurance may become "associate" members at $149 per year.

IMA benefits include a website, group health insurance and solo 401K retirement plans. Articles, newsletters and a therapist directory can be accessed on the IMA website. IMA members agree to abide by its Code of Ethics and may sign up for enrollment entirely online. The IMA has distinguished itself by creating a number of wellness divisions within their larger organization with similar benefits, affordability and liability coverage.

## Building Your Confidence

You're only brand new at something for a short while – try to enjoy your novice status while you've got it!

I remember starting out, literally trembling beside my first clients, terrified that I had no idea what I was doing. Now, giving a massage comes as naturally to me as breathing, and I cherish the memory of how nervous I once was. You may have this experience, too, and if so, here is some advice:

The best thing you can do is dive right in! Don't wait until you feel "ready" to begin giving massages. Though you may not feel confident enough to go out looking for clients right away, avoid the tendency to say "I need to practice on family and friends more first." At the beginning, make it a point to be as present and focused as you can for each and every session. If you focus on doing the best you can for each client, you will be amazed at how quickly your confidence builds over time.

At the outset, make a commitment to yourself and your practice to:
a.   Be Patient
b.   Practice Persistence - Keep Trying!
c.   Stay Professional in the Face of Adversity
d.   Don't Repeat Unsuccessful Behaviors – Adapt & Modify Your Approach
e.   Learn From Experience
f.   Have Fun & Don't Take Yourself Too Seriously

Take a job doing massage as soon as possible after receiving your credentials, even if it is only part-time. The more massages you can do, the better. With each session your confidence will grow, and before you know it, your nervousness and apprehension will disappear. Even if your goal is to open a private practice as soon as possible, consider working for a business with an established clientele for the experience, even if just for a short while.

Working in a busy spa or chiropractic office provides many benefits to the brand new massage therapist. First and foremost, you will have someone else drawing customers in so you can concentrate exclusively on your clients and learning. When shopping for an employer, look for a place with a good reputation and a thriving, full clientele. Besides making more money, the busier you are the more you will learn, and your confidence and skills will increase exponentially. Talk to other therapists in your area and ask them about the places they have worked. If you meet a happy crew of practitioners, chances are you will be happy in that environment as well.

Some therapists like to create a little opening ritual that they perform at the outset of a session. This can be as simple as standing over the client in the same place before beginning each session, or starting each session with the same opening strokes. Take some deep breaths and center yourself before making contact with your client. For better or worse, everything we are feeling passes through us and out of our hands. If you're feeling like a spaz, rest assured that your client will feel it. So, as they say, fake it till you make it! Be calm, be centered, be focused and it will show.

Practice your timing. A common learning curve when you are first starting out is losing track of time and suddenly realizing you have four minutes left to work on a client's entire upper body. In time, your sense of timing will become highly developed and you will know when an hour is up without even looking at a clock. Until then, take care to space your massage accordingly, dedicating a certain amount of time to each area before moving on. Mind your transitions and take care not to spend too much time on complicated draping. If a client has booked a full body massage, try not to get hung up on a specific area of the body (typically the back) at the expense of the rest of the body. If you notice one area in dire need of extra work, or the client specifically requests extra attention, don't hesitate to check in and see if it's alright with them if you skip certain areas in order to give them more focused work. Or, you can ask if they would like to extend their session so you have time to cover everything. Communication is key.

Dress in a way that makes you feel confident, and be on time or early for your client so you can be gathered and relaxed when you greet them. If, during the session, you feel like you made a mistake, just work with it. Don't say "oops" or "I goofed" or anything to that effect. Chances are your client won't even notice, and you never want a paying client to feel like you're practicing on them. Granted, when you are first starting out, your technique may not be the best. In the meantime, you do have control over much else. Resolve to be as focused as possible during each session, and strive to offer the absolute best in customer care. Concentrate on intention and establishing trust and rapport, and the rest will come with time.

Never be afraid to speak up if a client is asking for something beyond the scope of your abilities. Be confident in what you *can* provide, and cheerfully refer clients to other practitioners if they are asking for or require treatment that falls outside your level of expertise. The more confident you are in yourself, the more comfortable you will be in doing what is in the best interest of your client, even if it means referring them to another type of practitioner. View other therapists and health providers as colleagues and associates, not competition.

Massage therapy is a very personal service, so when someone says "no, thanks" to your offer of a massage or criticizes your work, it may be hard at first to separate your work from yourself. In other words, it may feel as if they are criticizing *you*. Always remind yourself that massage is a service like any other, and people say no to things all the time. Commonly their reasons have nothing to do with you; don't take it personally!

Try to surround yourself with positive people and minimize the time you spend with people who may not support your decision to pursue massage therapy as a career. Soon enough, the respect of colleagues and scores of happy, appreciative clients will provide all the reassurance you need that you made a great choice. Seek out a mentor; this may be someone in a healing field you admire, a skilled business person, or simply a supportive friend or colleague to share your experience. Once people have attained a high degree of accomplishment and success in their lives they love nothing more than to help others just starting out.

Learning to accept money from clients is challenging for some new therapists. Feelings of guilt may arise for being paid for something when, internally, you feel like you have no idea what you are doing. It can help to view money as a form of energy, meaningless until it is exchanged for something else of value. Trust that your caring touch, focused attention and massage are of great value to the person in your hands, and think of it simply as an exchange of energy. If you can't quite get your heart behind this concept, also keep in mind that we are all new at something in the beginning. Many corporate executives are being paid a lot more than you and they have no idea what they're doing either.

If you have difficulty with the notion of "selling" your massage, focus instead on selling your massage's benefits. For example, you are providing your client with lowered stress, a healthier frame of mind and a comfortable, relaxed body. If selling doesn't come naturally to you (and it doesn't for most therapists), keeping the emphasis on your client's health and happiness can make the process easier.

Lastly, maintain your sense of humor! Realize at the outset that setbacks and ridiculous things will happen, so learn to be okay with screwing up once in awhile. During my very first week doing professional massage, I was attempting a fancy draping technique to pull the client (ostensibly with grace) toward the edge of the table. Instead, I rolled her straight off onto the carpet. Not long after, trying out my new lotion-in-a-holster tool, I managed to spray lotion clear across the table, ultimately landing on the corner chair - all over the client's neatly folded clothing. Thankfully on both occasions the client was aware I was a newbie and reacted with understanding and great amusement. There is nothing like laughter to dissipate nerves and awkwardness. Today, when I have a client who is new to massage or who seems slightly uncomfortable, I use humor to break the ice, put them at ease and release their tension. Laughter *is* a wonderful medicine, and all the better if you can laugh at yourself, too!

# CHAPTER 5

## YOUR FIRST JOB

While you are still in massage school, begin some exploration of employment possibilities and give yourself a head start. Your school will often maintain a job board and instructors will usually have a good handle on employment options in the area. Get out and about and socialize with other people in the industry. Part of the magic of the massage field is that there are so many avenues you might take; you may read an article, meet a practitioner at a conference, or get a new client that may capture your imagination, give you a new opportunity or set you off in a direction you never knew existed.

Read up on spas or employers before you contact them so you come across as interested and informed. At a minimum, visit their website and familiarize yourself with their treatments and services. When you are contacting a potential employer or hiring manager, be persistent without being a nuisance. Obtain the hiring manager's name so you may send your resume addressed directly to them at their office or via email. It shows great interest and initiative to seek out the name of the person who will be reviewing and reading your resume, and sets you apart from the applicants who may settle for the generic, 'to whom it may concern' style cover letters.

By the time you complete massage school and your required practice hours, you may have an inkling of what kind of massage and bodywork you are drawn to...

Here are some examples of the career paths you might take:

## Day Spas and Salons

The ubiquity and popularity of day spas and salons make them excellent employment choices for the new therapist. The many thousands of day spas, salons and massage franchises that have opened across the United States vary in size, location and services they offer. Today, you can find luxurious day spas in major cities, community-serving suburban salons, and massage clinics in strip malls. The opportunities for career positions in these settings are enormous; day spas and salons are the number one employer of massage therapists in the United States. They make an ideal first place of employment due to the sheer number and variety of people you will come into contact with. Some guests will expect serious muscle therapy, while others only wish to relax; one guest will be fit and athletic and the next a couch potato. In the course of working in a spa, salon or massage clinic, you will learn to be adaptable, a crucial skill for any therapist to possess.

Modern spa settings are structured and streamlined so that therapists can focus on doing what they do best – their interaction and work with each client – while everything else is provided for them. Additionally, spa menus have become quite extensive and creative in their offerings. Many spas will encourage you to learn other treatment modalities in the course of your employment and further enhance your skills.

Depending on the size of the spa, you may or may not be offered any kind of benefits, so it is very important to review and understand this information when you are first being hired. Make sure to ask if they provide any full or partial benefits, such as disability or health insurance, either immediately upon hire or after a certain period of employment (e.g. after ninety days, six months, etc.).

Many therapists begin their career as part of these organizations, with the ultimate goal to establish their own private practice one day. If this is you, and you're looking at your spa work as "experience," do your best to show respect and gratitude to your employer during the time you are with them by maintaining a good attitude and doing great work.

## Resorts and Hotels

Massage therapy and spa services have become so popular that they are now expected amenities at most fine hotels and resorts. Spas are viewed as a necessity for resort developments and new hotel openings in most cities, providing many job opportunities for massage therapists within the larger hospitality industry.

Working in a resort or hotel is unique in that every week is different and you will be meeting various people from all over the country or world. Most resorts and hotel groups are in a position to offer a well-rounded benefits package as well as disability and health insurance. If you work for an established hotel group or chain, you may be able to receive travel discounts, relocation opportunities, or the ability to split your work schedule between multiple properties.

The hospitality industry – especially among the larger hotel groups – tends to allow for and encourage career growth. If you have an interest in ultimately expanding your massage career into management or other spa roles, establishing yourself in a resort or hotel position can be an excellent choice.

## Destination Spas

Destination spas give you the opportunity to work in a gorgeous, serene setting with a sophisticated and discerning clientele. Destination spas only account for a small percentage of spas nationwide, so it is likely you may need to relocate to take a position with one of them. Unlike day spas, destination spas are exclusive locations where guests often stay for one week or more at a time, a vacation that is dedicated to health, fitness, healthy living, and relaxation.

Working for a destination spa will often provide you with a solid benefits package, looks great on a resume, and may potentially provide you with career growth and relocation opportunities if the ownership maintains other resorts and properties.

## Medi-Spas

Medical and dental spas (commonly known as "medi-spas") have experienced a great deal of growth in recent years. In these organizations, a licensed physician or dentist is typically an owner or on staff; this allows for certain treatments to be practiced in the spa that normally couldn't be offered in a regular day spa. For example, a medical spa may offer various laser and injectable treatments (Botox, for example) that can only be done under the licensed supervision of a doctor or nurse.

Medical spas are typically very high-tech and cutting edge, and commonly overseen by a plastic surgeon or dermatologist. If you have an interest in aesthetics and enjoy working with the most modern tools available, a career in this setting may be a perfect fit for you. Dental spas are also growing in popularity, offering treatments to help overcome the anxiety and stress a dental visit evokes in some individuals. Massage therapy can be a wonderful compliment to those already practicing as dental hygienists, mixing up the work week and creating an additional source of income. In both dental and medical spa settings, it is likely your massage work will emphasize relaxation and restoration, preparing a client for surgery or helping them recover afterward.

## Chiropractic and Medical Offices

A number of therapists have created thriving careers in massage therapy working exclusively with a chiropractic or medical group. In these settings, the group typically provides clients who you work with as an employee or independent contractor, depending on the terms you create and agree to.

One of the tremendous upsides to this type of work is that the group typically bills insurance for its clients, giving many individuals access to massage treatments who could otherwise not afford it. Additionally, the administrative staff will often do the billing for you, eliminating what would otherwise be a lot of paperwork. If you have the opportunity to learn how to do insurance billing, take advantage! This knowledge may come in handy one day if you decide to branch out on your own and open an independent office.

Depending on the group, you may be expected to perform shorter massage treatments (20-25 minutes in length), or regular long sessions (60 or 90 minutes). These different length sessions will appeal differently to each therapist, so set out to create what works best for your clients, the needs of the group, and your style of work.

You may receive benefits or not in this work setting, so be sure to discuss your overall employment package with the group just as you would in a spa setting. Once all the parties come to an agreement, be sure to put it in writing and maintain a copy for your records. If your ultimate goal is to one day have your own private practice, make sure that your employment agreement does not contain any overly restrictive non-compete terms.

## Gyms, Health Clubs and Fitness Centers

If you enjoy working with athletes and are knowledgeable about many different sports, activities and how they impact the human body you may wish to establish your practice within one of these businesses. Working with athletes, you will need to be aware of training schedules and how to adapt your massage around training and competitions or races. This type of work can be a lot of fun and always interesting if you are into sports and fitness in your own life, as you will no doubt be discussing training tips, nutrition, schedules and related topics with your clients. These work settings will also give you plenty of opportunities to provide public demonstrations, offer seminars, provide chair massage introductions, and give free educational talks to the membership.

Some gyms emphasize free weights or bodybuilding and may draw a larger percentage of male clients. Others will offer more group classes, including aerobics, yoga and pilates and may attract more female members. Keep these things in mind, as the members will be your clients, too!

You may opt to begin as an employee at these locations, and once you're established become a contractor and instead rent space within the larger facility. Sometimes you will be given a free gym membership as part of your employment package; this not only saves you some money but also provides you with numerous networking and marketing opportunities with fellow members while you're working out. Another option – typically once you've gotten some experience under your belt – is to become the designated massage therapist for a team or professional athlete. This can be a fantastic opportunity for your career resume as well as give you the opportunity to travel. Volunteering to provide chair massage services at competitions such as triathlons, bike or running races is a great way to pick up some sports-minded clientele. Network with other local fitness providers, personal trainers, nutritionists and sporting goods stores so that you can refer clients among one another.

## Hospitals and Hospice Work

Building a massage therapy career in hospital or hospice settings is a highly challenging yet extremely rewarding path. The clients you will work with in these settings will often be extremely ill, injured or dying. It can be emotionally difficult to manage, as you will no doubt become close and attached to your clients as all therapists do. However, to be with people - to listen and give care and compassion - during the most challenging time in their lives can be absolutely fulfilling. When people are hurt or ill, they may feel more afraid and alone than ever before. Working in these settings, you will be making a difference in people's lives, often at a time when it matters most.

Many nurses opt to study massage therapy to expand on their skills and further care for their patients. In fact, it was a nurse named Delores Krieger who introduced healing touch – a modality known as Therapeutic Touch – in a widespread and systematic fashion, teaching other nurses this healing adjunct. Akin to energy work, Therapeutic Touch directs the therapist to work in the client's energy field or aura. This makes Therapeutic Touch widely accessible to the greatest number of hospitalized clients, many of whom have a limited range of motion or ability to be touched.

If you are drawn to this type of work, the first step is to call or visit a hospital or hospice and inquire if they currently have massage therapists on staff. If not, many of them will welcome volunteer therapists, and occasionally these roles can turn into a paid position with some time and persistence. Once management has the opportunity to see the difference you make in the lives of their patients, they may find a way to make your presence a permanent one.

## On-site or Corporate Massage

Compared to other workplace settings, on-site or corporate massage can provide a very social environment that is well-suited for personable, outgoing therapists. On-site massage is commonly performed in a specialized massage chair that holds the client upright and comfortably seated. The sessions are usually done in shorter durations (10-20 minutes), giving you the ability to see many different clients within the same shift. Many massage schools offer specific classes and workshops in chair massage, and these opportunities can be a great investment to your practice.

On-site massage is ideal for high-traffic, public locations where clients have limited time and need to keep their clothing on during the session. Office buildings, airports, malls, grocery stores, farmer's markets and fairs are all fantastic settings for chair massage work. You can also promote chair massage for holiday work parties, store openings and special events. People love massage in any form and at these events you will likely find an enthusiastic line clamoring for your services. Placement is very important; when arranging details with the owner or manager of the location, be sure to emphasize the importance of being visible. Don't get stuck behind a wall or hidden away in the bathroom hallway. Arrive early and get to know the surrounding businesses and employees so they can talk you up and send people your way.

If you're just testing the waters, you can typically rent a massage chair from your local massage supply store. If you plan to do regular chair massage it may be worth it for you to purchase a chair of your own.

Before settling on one, try out different models for ease of transport, comfort and simplicity of use. Is it lightweight? Does the cover come with wheels on it? Will it fit easily in your car? Sit on it. Imagine you are the client. Is it comfortable? Does the chair adjust easily to accommodate all body types and sizes? Can you set it up and re-fold it within a few minutes?

On-site massage can be an excellent complement to your other massage employment and is a wonderful marketing tool. It gets you out in the public eye and meeting people in the context of massage. Be sure to take your business cards and brochures along with you and encourage your clients to book a table session with you in the future. Let them know where you regularly work and make it easy for them to reach you.

Pay structure and terms for on-site work will vary depending on the location and clientele. In some settings, each individual client will be expected to pay you, and in this case you may want to charge by the minute or have a flat fee for a certain amount of time. For example, you could charge $1 per minute, or $20 for fifteen minutes. However, if you are working on a company's employees, and being paid by the company, you may wish to set a flat hourly rate with a minimum number of hours. For instance, you may bill a company $50 an hour to provide chair massage, with a minimum of three hours. This way, even if no employees turn up to receive your services, you will still be guaranteed a certain amount of pay for your time.

I have learned from experience that the smaller the amount of the bill, the more likely a client is to bounce a check. You may find this to be true or not, but I have learned to accept cash only when doing chair massage at a party or event where clients are paying on an individual basis. It is maddening to pay bounced check fees on a check that was only for $15; get a few of those and you can quickly wind up in the hole! With the ubiquity of ATMs today it is not too much to ask your clients to pay you in cash when offering chair massage.

Finally, chair massage can be a lot of fun if you are willing to be flexible. I have personally done chair massage at all-night raves, festive company holiday parties and sophisticated art gallery openings. If you are the kind of person who requires a highly structured atmosphere or regulated setting when it comes to temperature, noise level and music, you may need to adopt more of a go-with-the-flow attitude when it comes to on-site massage! If you are willing to adapt, you may really come to enjoy this social and lucrative type of massage career.

## Physical Therapy, Sports Medicine and Pain Management Centers

A career in one of these facilities will be appealing if you relish working with specific issues, physical ailments, injuries and rehabilitation. Therapists working in these settings are very knowledgeable about anatomy and the body's physical systems. If you enjoy working with specific problems and don't mind some degree of repetition (seeing the same clients repeatedly or working on the same issue over time) this could be an excellent career choice for you. Another benefit of this type of massage work is that it may be covered by a client's health insurance or health savings plan, increasing your client base by making your sessions more affordable.

## Volunteer Work

Volunteering is a fantastic way to immediately bridge the gap between becoming certified in massage and beginning your first massage job. It will not only give you the ability to jump in and gain experience quickly, but the clients you work with in a volunteer capacity will often be among your most special and cherished.

Hospitals, hospices, elder-care facilities, homeless shelters and domestic violence agencies are among the many organizations who welcome volunteer massage therapists. You may also explore becoming a first responder for natural disasters or crises through relief organizations or local charities.

### DON'T HAVE A CLUE AS TO WHAT KIND OF MASSAGE YOU GRAVITATE TOWARD?

No problem! Most therapists just graduating from massage school fall into this camp. This may simply signal that you will be more of a generalist, a sign you're flexible and can accommodate many different types of clients. You may wish to look for your first position in a day spa, resort or massage and wellness center. In these settings, you will gain exposure to a wide array of clients, body types, and massage modalities. Spa work requires a special type of flexibility, since each client will be physically different as well as coming in for a very different reason. It is an excellent training ground and first job in the field because you will get a sampling of everything!

Regardless of where you work or the style of massage you practice, it is a tremendous lesson to learn how to listen, intuit, and tailor your massage specifically to different clients and personalities. This will become a priceless skill you will carry with you throughout your career. Many spa and resort employers will ask that you become proficient in several different types of massage and body treatments, and sometimes they will even train and pay you to do so!

While I was still in massage school, I took a part-time job working at the front desk of a massage wellness center. In this position I booked appointments, greeted visitors, received client payments, scheduled the therapists, and dealt with all kinds of unexpected occurrences....

> "Fire in Room 6!"
>
> "No ma'am, I'm sorry you can't bring your cat in to be massaged..."

Little did I know what a valuable opportunity this job would be in learning about the business side of massage therapy. I got to know many practitioners and witnessed the good, the bad and occasionally, the just plain weird. I learned what motivated customers to re-book, to tip, to cancel or to stay loyal to a certain therapist. I was able to trade sessions with many of the therapists, and improve thanks to their technique and feedback. I acquired the skill of speaking to potential clients on the telephone, determining their motivation to get a massage and then matching them with the appropriate therapist. I learned to read callers and discern whether they were looking for a sexual rather than therapeutic massage. I also learned plenty about the seasonality of massage, from August (*hellloooo*, is anybody home?) to Valentine's Day (*sold out!*)

If you can manage it, I highly recommend working or interning prior to or during your massage training. While the pay will be relatively minimal ($8-$12/hour on average), the things you learn will be invaluable to later establishing your own successful practice.

## Getting Hired: The Application and Interview Process

Most employers request that your first point of contact is submitting a current resume, either by mail, email or in person. If they specify how they would prefer to receive it (by email, for example), try to follow their instructions and demonstrate that you have read the entire job posting and can follow directions. Try to tailor your resume for each particular job opportunity, taking care to read and incorporate the skills and strengths they are looking for in a new hire. Many employers are wary of attachments sent over the internet because of computer viruses, so if they request that your resume be "in line" or within the email, be sure to do so. Many people now simply delete emails with attachments.

Personally, I prefer taking a resume by in person. It gives you a chance to meet the receptionist and a staff member or two, as well as observe the facility. Does the staff seem friendly and happy? Are they busy? Is the parking lot full? You can learn a lot of information from this initial visit that will help you prepare for a later interview. While you're there, find out who manages hiring and ask if you could have one of their business cards. Then, a day or two later, send an email or leave a voicemail for that person to follow-up, letting them know you delivered a resume and are very interested in the position.

When you are applying for your first massage therapist job, it is understandable that your work history may be entirely unrelated to massage. Instead, emphasize your experience in massage school, as well as elements in your prior jobs that may successfully overlap with the job you are applying for. For example, you may have experience as a nursery school teacher. To be a successful nursery school teacher you must be nurturing, patient and responsible, which happen to be wonderful attributes to have as a massage therapist. Choose your personal and professional references carefully, and give them a heads up ahead of time so they're not taken by surprise when an employer calls. If you're applying for your first massage position, you may wish to use one or two of your massage school instructors or experienced therapists as your professional references.

If you get called in for an interview, prepare! Do some research online or in your community so you have some familiarity and thoughtful questions to ask the interviewer. Dress neatly, professionally and appropriately. While you need not wear a suit and carry a briefcase, you should also not wear flip flops and a tank top. Bring a few copies of your resume along with you to the interview just in case some additional staff members wind up joining you. Unless the interviewer brings it up, avoid lengthy salary or pay discussions during your first interview. Instead, ask questions that will better inform you about the company, the culture and the specific job responsibilities. You can inquire about pay *after* you are offered a position.

Many spa managers and trainers will request that you perform a demonstration or test massage as part of their interview process. A few of the things they are typically looking for during a demo massage are:

a.   Do you listen to what they are asking for?

b.   Are you thorough in the performance of the massage, including the draping and transitions?

c.   Are you focused?

d.   Is your "bedside manner" and communication clear, warm and direct?

e.   What level of skill and confidence is coming through your hands?

It is completely natural to feel nervous when you are giving a test massage; most managers know this and will take time to help put you at ease. Even if you are new and less skilled than other therapists, having a sunny, positive attitude may make all the difference. Take feedback and criticism of your massage constructively. Listening calmly and carefully to feedback and reacting proactively shows you care, have confidence in your potential and are willing to grow. Finding these traits in a new therapist is an employer's dream come true!

There are a few things you will want to ascertain about the position during your interview. Will you be expected to perform massage therapy only? Which modalities are most requested? How long are the shifts for massage therapists? Will you be able to learn body wraps or treatments as well? If you're not booked, will you have other responsibilities such as selling product, cleaning, or answering the phone? The day after the interview, send a brief thank you letter to your interviewer to acknowledge them for their time and consideration. While email communication is common and acceptable, you can really set yourself apart by sending a handwritten notecard.

Once you are offered a job, take your time and carefully read the employment contract. Most employers will understand if you would like some time to review it, or have someone else such as a lawyer look it over. If the request for time appears to bend them out of shape that could either be a sign that something is amiss or that they are desperate to hire you. Make note of it, but don't allow it to pressure you into signing anything on the spot.

When reviewing the terms of your job offer, make sure you understand the following as it pertains to your employment:

• Are any partial or full benefits offered? (Medical, dental, worker's compensation insurance, disability insurance)

- Do the benefits begin immediately or after a certain period of employment? (90 days, six months, etc.)
- Are you expected to pay for part of your benefits? (You want to know if a portion of your paycheck will be deducted and put toward your benefits package.)
- Does your employment include sick days or paid vacation? If not, can you earn the ability to accrue these benefits over time?
- Does your contract contain a "non-compete clause?" In other words, will you be allowed to work wherever you like in the event you discontinue your employment?

## A Note on Pay…

A common complaint among massage therapists, especially in spa positions, is how much they get paid compared to what the guest of the spa or resort is actually paying for the service. Please note, while the spa industry may *look* glamorous from the outside, make no mistake that it is an extremely challenging business to run. Spas in particular have very high operating expenses and low profit margins compared to other industries. You – meaning the therapists and practitioners of a spa - account for the single largest expense the business must contend with: payroll. When your employer pays you, he/she is also often paying out in benefits, taxes, worker's compensation and insurance on your behalf as well. The expense of having you as an employee is far greater than the amount you see on your paycheck.

Therapist pay is unfortunately an oft-griped about topic among spa employees, but if most therapists knew the true costs of operating the business they may view their employment in a different light. If you think about all the things you *don't* have to contend with or pay for – laundry, sheets, robes, slippers, advertising, marketing, cleaning services – you may find, in reality, that your pay is quite generous.

In a field as personal as massage therapy, your attitude is immensely important to your success. Positive thinking is infectious, as is negative thinking; which condition would you rather be working in? Create the upbeat, supportive work environment you want by playing a positive role among your colleagues and coworkers.

## Employee vs. Independent Contractor

Regardless of where you apply to work, make sure you understand before you are hired whether you will be an *employee* or an *independent contractor.* There are important differences between them and advantages and disadvantages to each. It is vital that you understand those differences and how they apply to you.

As an employee, you will be given a schedule and occasionally be eligible for health care benefits, worker's compensation, disability and other perks. Your social security, state and federal taxes will automatically be taken out of your paycheck, which is ideal if you don't like dealing with records and receipts. As an employee you can give your full and undivided attention to your clients without worrying about many business details, and you will usually make some money even if you don't have any clients in a day. The company's management will typically handle all marketing and advertising, which is also an advantage if you're just starting out. All supplies, linens and laundry service are usually provided for you – never underestimate the value of having someone else do your laundry!

The downside of being an employee is that you will be expected to work a relatively fixed schedule, occasionally long hours, and your pay will be a fraction of what you could make as an independent bodyworker. For many therapists, though, the benefits of being an employee far outweigh the cons, especially for new or inexperienced practitioners.

If you are working for someone else as an employee, the situation will invariably arise where a client asks you for your business card with the intention of booking a session outside of the workplace and paying you directly. They will usually request that you work on them in their home, or ask if they can visit your home or office. It is easier to handle this situation when it arises if your employer has voiced how they feel about this occurrence. Some employers strictly frown upon it and take pains to prevent it by having their staff sign non-compete agreements. Other employers understand that it is bound to happen occasionally, look the other way, or support it to some extent. Remember, when you see a client while you are working as an employee, that client is technically a client of the spa, clinic or salon where you are working. Your best bet is to communicate clearly with your manager and adhere to their policy, whatever it may be.

As an independent contractor, you have the right to set your own hours and therefore have a more independent, flexible schedule. In essence, you are renting the space from the owner for the time you are working. Benefits such as disability, health or worker's compensation insurance are usually not offered. You are typically responsible for maintaining your own liability insurance and paying your own social security, self-employment, state and federal taxes. As a contractor, you will only be paid for the sessions you actually do, and may be responsible for some of your own marketing expenses. Linens, supplies and laundry are typically up to you as well.

You will almost always make more money per session as an independent contractor since you, not the owner, are responsible for paying taxes on the income you generate. However, you trade more money for much more responsibility. Working as a contractor also gives you the ability to work multiple places; many therapists split their time being a contractor and an independent practitioner in private practice, seeing the same clients at either location.

As an independent contractor, it is vitally important that you keep track of your income and receipts to write off the appropriate expenses (also known as deductions.) A CPA or accountant experienced in working with massage therapists can be of great help. Ask around experienced therapists for the names of some good referrals.

If you are working under someone else's business or massage license, take a moment to check the authenticity and validity of their license. Remember, as an independent contractor you are in essence running your own business, so protect yourself and refrain from "taking someone's word for it." Even though it is someone else's business and license that is in question, it is up to you to make sure you are protected and working legally. Otherwise you could get in trouble and penalized right along with your employer.

# CHAPTER 6

## WORKING INDEPENDENTLY
## WITH HOTELS, INNS & RESORTS

If you live in a major city or an area that draws a lot of tourists, conference attendees or business travelers, working as an independent contractor with hotels, resorts and bed & breakfast inns can be a wonderful market to focus or extend your massage practice.

Advantages of this type of work are:
- Very independent, flexible schedule: You set your own hours and decide whether or not to take each booking
- Interesting and varied clientele: Allows you to meet new people from all over the country or world
- Constant professional growth: This style of work builds your practice and skills in that you're always working with different bodies and personalities, requiring a high level of adaptability
- Medium to high pay: Often you will make in one session what you would make during an entire shift at a spa, especially so at luxury hotels

Disadvantages:
- Unpredictable scheduling: Clients often book with only a few hours notice, so the ability to get up and go is important. Keeping a cell phone handy and massage table/supplies in your car is ideal.
- Seasonality: This type of work will require that you adapt to busy and slow periods. The concierge, along with practical experience, will show you which days and months are busier than others. Over time, you may wish to schedule the bulk of your private practice clients or other work during the hotel "slow days."
- Dragging your table around: Keeping a table and supplies in your car can be very helpful in this respect. Purchase a lightweight table designed for frequent travel and a bag with wheels or a sturdy shoulder strap. Some hotels may even be open to providing a table, linens and workspace for you on location. Also, if you establish close working relationships with a select few hotels you will minimize having to run all over

town from appointment to appointment. In other words, it is better to work often and exclusively with a few properties than a little bit with a lot of them.

- It's just you: By this I mean you do without the camaraderie and support present in many spas or massage therapy establishments. You will need to be self-motivated and, if it is important to you, explore other means of career support through classes, professional associations, club memberships, and friendships with fellow massage therapists.

## How to Get Your Foot in the Door

Many travelers – both business and recreational – have come to expect that spa services will be available to them at their hotel or inn. Property developers have responded to this expectation, and most new resorts and fine hotels include an in-house spa. However, smaller boutique hotels, inns and bed & breakfasts rely on independent practitioners to provide massage therapy for their guests; these properties can be excellent partners for your practice.

It is important that you meet, make a good impression and cultivate relationships with the concierge staff at the hotel or resort. In most cases they will be the middle men/women and guests will book massage appointments exclusively through them. In a smaller hotel or inn, you will most often be approaching the owner or manager of the property.

Concierges and hospitality managers have very busy, demanding jobs, especially during the peak travel seasons in your area. They will often have limited time to speak with you, so it is best to schedule a meeting with them rather than drop in unannounced. Because of the stress and fast pace of their work, they are often in dire need of a massage! Offering a demo massage to the head concierge is a great way to get their attention, get to know them, and demonstrate your work and professionalism. The senior concierges typically work weekdays, and often the best time to visit them is in the early afternoon. Avoid trying to get their attention during busy times such as check-in, check-out, weekends and holidays.

When deciding whether to work with a particular hotel, pay attention to parking arrangements and expenses and remember to build them into your rates. Ask the concierge what their rate and parking policy is, and if they have none, work together to reach an agreement. Anything you can do to make their job easier will be appreciated.

The concierge or hotel manager is your gateway to this type of work – the better they know you and your work the busier they will keep you!

> *If there is a particular place you would *really* love to work, don't go there first! Instead, pitch your services to a few other places first. After you present yourself and your work a few times you will not only be more confident and have a more effective pitch, you will also know what questions come up and be better prepared.

## Marketing Materials

At a minimum, you should have a professional business card for the hotel staff to keep at the front desk. You may also want to provide a flyer that details your experience and the types of massage you are skilled in. Sometimes a hotel or inn will even allow you to place your brochure in the individual hotel rooms, whereby the guests can call and book with you directly.

If a hotel or resort has a full service spa, this does not necessarily preclude you from working there. You can offer your services on an on-call basis, for example in the evening when the spa is closed or when the spa happens to be booked solid. Occasionally guests prefer to have their massage performed in their hotel room rather than the spa, and some hotel spas limit their employees from working outside the spa for liability reasons. In these instances, as an independent contractor, you can offer your services to those guests specifically requesting in-room massage.

Please remember, you are your own best advertisement! The first few sessions you complete for a hotel will speak much louder than your marketing materials. If you consistently show up on time, are professional, dressed neatly, and a pleasure to deal with, you will be the first therapist in the staff's mind when a guest requests a massage.

## Tips on Working in the Hotel & Resort Market

It is important that you project a professional image at all times, and that this is reflected in your dress, punctuality, and rapport with clients, staff, and hotel guests. This is especially true when working at luxury or high-end hotels and inns, where customer service and the appearance of such is even more important than in other places.

Always be on time, as these clients are often on a strict time table, especially so for business travelers. Even if you have extra time, if the client schedules an hour massage, you should stick to an hour massage unless they specifically request extending the session. Clients will often need to be somewhere immediately afterward and are counting on you to finish on time. While you may think you're doing them a favor by giving them extra time free of charge, it may inconvenience them or make them late.

Be adaptable! Some clients, especially tourists, are in your city to relax and enjoy. Often they will want to chat throughout the session and learn about things to do in the area. Other clients, however, are in the midst of a demanding schedule and need to unwind from meetings and jetlag. These clients tend to prefer more limited conversation or silence. Try to pay attention to their verbal and nonverbal cues and adapt your work accordingly.

Remember, guests come first! If you are waiting at the front desk to begin a massage or be paid for a completed session and a guest appears, be mindful that their needs come first. Always be considerate and wait until the staff is free to attend to you. After dealing with numerous requests and demands throughout their shift, the staff will certainly appreciate your grace and patience.

If it has been slow for awhile and you haven't received any calls from a particular hotel for some time, don't be afraid to give the concierge a call and let them know you are available. Be careful not to do this so often as to be a nuisance, but a gentle reminder once in awhile will put you (and offering massage to their guests) in the forefront of their minds.

## Payment & Gratuities

Each hotel may have a different method of payment for massage therapy services. They may ask the guest to pay you directly, or they may have them sign off on payment slips so they can add the charges directly to their room bill. Some hotels will allow you to set your own rates, while others will set the rates for massage therapy themselves.

If the hotel does not do so already, or allows you to set your own rates, you may want to charge more for early morning or late night appointments (e.g. sessions beginning before 9AM or after 10PM).

It is also important that you set a cancellation policy with the hotel if they do not have one in place. This may range from four to forty-eight hours, in most cases, and is important because otherwise many tourists think it is perfectly alright to change plans last minute with little or no notice. With an established cancellation policy, if a guest cancels or does not show up for their appointment within the timeframe mandated by the cancellation policy you can get paid regardless.

Especially in urban or touristy areas, it is standard practice for the massage therapist to provide a cut of their payment to the concierge staff or the individual concierge who booked the appointment. Some hotels have established a standard commission, while others will leave the amount up to the therapist. If it is not a standard amount, try to learn what the other therapists give so you can match it.

Most guests will include a gratuity without prompting, but often you may draw a line on the paid-out slip where they may write one in. You may also ask for guidance on this from the concierge staff. Remember that many guests from parts of Europe, Australia or Asia do not realize that tipping is normal practice in the United States, so don't take it personally if someone fails to tip you. Usually they just haven't read their tour guide books thoroughly enough!

## Helpful Hints

Working at hotels has a special angle that is worth mentioning, especially for new or inexperienced therapists. While we have come a long way in establishing massage therapy as a professional health care practice, there are some individuals who still associate massage with sex or prostitution. Keep in mind that hotel guests are away from home, in an anonymous place, and therefore may act in a way they never would around someone they knew or might expect to see again. Also, people coming from other cultures may mistake the therapeutic nature of our work because it is practiced differently in the culture they are coming from.

On most occasions you will be working entirely alone with the guest, either in their hotel room or a treatment room provided by the hotel. For safety reasons, it is imperative you carry yourself with confidence and have some experience behind you, especially so if you are female.

None of this is reason enough to shy away from this kind of work—the vast majority of guests expect and greatly value a therapeutic massage— but it is something to be aware of. Always keeping good boundaries and setting a professional, no-nonsense tone from the start will help minimize this issue.

## Remember to Take Time Off

Remember to take care of yourself. The nature of hospitality work is cyclical; it can be extremely busy or slow, and you may have an avalanche of calls at once or none at all. Because of this, you may be tempted to work every time you get a call. Try not to wind up working seven days a week and build a dedicated day or two off into your week to give your body a break.

Many therapists, especially those just starting out, are working in a spa or two and trying to build a private practice all at the same time! Every now and then take some time to assess your goals, energy level, and the balance you would like to attain between work and life. Be strategic about your work schedule and plan for your long-term health and happiness in a massage career.

## Summary List of Things to Address with the Manager or Concierge Staff

*Payment:* Is the rate for massage therapy set by the hotel, or do you get to make it? (The average rack rate – or standard room rate – at the hotel can offer guidance in how much you charge for a massage. For example, if a room costs $600 a night, then $150 for an in-room massage sounds reasonable. If a room costs $120 per night, it is less likely a guest of that hotel will pay $150 for a massage.) Does the guest pay you directly in cash, or do the charges get added to their room bill? Can you charge additionally for early morning, late night or holiday appointments?

*Gratuities:* Can guests add a gratuity to the paid-out slip?

*Parking:* Where is the best place to park? Will the hotel keep your car for you? What are the charges for parking? If you have to park in a garage or some ways away, is it alright for you to drop your table off prior to parking?

*Location of Sessions:* Will you primarily work in the guest rooms or is there a separate dedicated massage room? Are all the guest rooms large enough to accommodate a massage table?

*Cancellation Policy:* Does the hotel have one? If not, work with the hotel staff to put a reasonable cancellation policy in place. Cancellation policies typically range from four hours to forty-eight hours in advance, depending on the location.

*Method of Payment:* If the hotel accepts payments, you will usually be paid out in cash. However, if the guests pay you directly you must decide what forms of payment you will accept so that the guest may be informed ahead of time. My personal policy has been not to accept checks and receive cash only, but you may feel differently depending on your location. If you opt to accept credit cards through mobile technology applications, test it well enough before you see clients so you're certain it works properly.

*Sheets:* Are you responsible for bringing your own linens or is the hotel policy to provide them? Sometimes hotels and inns will deliver a set of twin sheets to the room prior to your arrival. It is great not to have to carry a lot of sheets around and will really save you on laundry expenses. If a hotel offers to provide you with linens, by all means, take them up on it!

Working with hotels and resorts can be a very fun, lucrative and rewarding path for your massage practice. If the spontaneous and varied nature of this work is for you, remember to cherish the concierge and staff who handle your promotion and bookings. You will come to depend on them, and it's vital that you maintain a close working relationship. Remember to appreciate them every chance you get!

# CHAPTER 7

## GOING OUT ON YOUR OWN: LAUNCHING AN INDEPENDENT PRACTICE

Many practitioners excel working as employees in a group environment, such as in a spa, medical office, or otherwise being part of a massage crew. As discussed in Chapter 5, the benefits of a team atmosphere and employee status are many. A number of massage therapists are happy to build their practice entirely within the umbrella of a larger organization, but others feel the entrepreneurial call to go out on their own. Just as with your decision where to attend massage school, it behooves you to take some time to research, budget and strategize your move to independent status… careful planning will save you many headaches!

### Plan, plan, plan!

Before you make the move to independent status, create a business plan that will address all the facets of your new venture. A business plan is a vital tool that will help shape your business and give you a realistic snapshot of the cost of opening and initially sustaining your practice. Operating your own office space and practice is an expensive undertaking and requires a great deal of commitment. Crafting a business plan will force you to look at the nitty gritty details and realities that we may ignore while we are swept up in the idea of our new massage office. The business plan need not be an overwhelming volume to be effective. To help get you started, I've outlined the key expenses below in a condensed format. (Hint! Many of these expenses can also be tax deductions, so your business planning can do double duty and help you get ready for tax time.) Go through every item and check each one that will be applicable to you. Then, put an estimated cost next to each one. When you are finished, total them up for a reasonable estimate of your start-up expenses.

*Lease / Office Expenses – Initial Down Payment + On-going*
You will need to budget, plan and search for an office where you will provide your massage sessions. Overhead expenses include everything that goes into leasing and maintaining your office space. Your office expense includes both start-up costs (typically your first month's rent

plus security deposit, and occasionally multiple month's rent in advance) and on-going expenses (your monthly payment.)

*Massage table and supplies*
In addition to your table, you may be investing in oils, lotions, linens, sheets, blankets, towels, massage tools, essential oils, pillows and bolsters, music, posters, anatomical charts, lighting and décor. When buying supplies, be sure to check the retailer's return policy and manufacturer warranties, especially when you're dealing with big ticket items and things you will use for a long time.

*Books and subscriptions*
You may order magazine subscriptions or purchase books for your massage office.

*Website and related expenses*
Be sure to include related costs such as your hosting service, internet connection (dial-up, cable or broadband) and email service.

*Computer, printer, software, fax machine*

*Work telephone*
You may wish to use your mobile phone as your office number, or have an office line installed at your new location. Keep in mind that many telephone companies charge much higher rates for business lines than residential lines, so check it out in advance!

*Liability insurance*

*Business and general liability insurance*
If this is your first time leasing office space, you will need to educate yourself about insuring commercial space. Get quotes from several reputable insurance companies before committing to one.

*Marketing Materials*
These may include your business cards, brochures, postcards, flyers, grand opening announcements, and more…

*Design Costs*
Estimate the costs for a graphic designer to create your marketing materials and web designer your website, if applicable.

*Postage for client mailings*

*Credit Card Processing Service & Merchant Account Fees*
Necessary if you plan to accept credit cards in your practice.

*Furnishings & Decorations*
These may include a couch, chair(s), clothing rack or hanger, laundry
hamper, rug or carpet, stereo system, and more…

*Office supplies*
Paper, pens, paper clips, and all the other supplies you'll need for your
office.

*Water*
Bottled or water service if you plan to have it in your office.

*Signage*
Some commercial spaces require that you provide a certain type of
signage as a condition of your lease, and these can be surprisingly
expensive depending on the size and materials involved. Again, check it
out before signing a lease.

*Electricity, Garbage, & Cleaning / Janitorial*
Your landlord or the previous tenant should be able to give you a rough
estimate of these monthly or quarterly bills.

*Business License, if required*

*City / County / State Permits, if required*

*Linens, Towels & Sheets*
Quality massage sheets can get expensive quickly, so shop around for the
best deals and don't buy in bulk before you test them and know for sure
that you like them. You can find sheets specifically cut for massage tables
at massage supply stores and online. Regular twin-sized sheets usually
work well for most tables; you may find high quality sheets at a lowered
cost at discount stores such as Ross, Marshalls and TJ Maxx. Often these
sheets are discounted because they are marked *irregular* or have a small,
inconsequential defect – just in case, keep your receipts and check them
out before using them in case you need to return them.

*Laundry*
You may decide to do your own laundry at a laundromat, purchase a

washer and dryer to keep in your office, or use a laundry service. Weigh the pros, cons and expense of each option to decide which is best for you.

Final words of advice on business planning....

- Remember to budget your personal living expenses, and be realistic. Figure out what your lifestyle actually costs on a monthly basis and budget that into your first-year business plan. The first year of operating your own business is a great time to cut down on personal living expenses, so this can be a well-timed exercise and make visible some expenses that may be reduced or eliminated.
- Things nearly always take longer than you think they will. For example, if you want to open your office in four weeks, estimate it to be more like six-to-eight weeks. If your web developer says the website will be finished in six weeks, you can realistically assume it might take three months. You may be an exception to the rule and everything may come together perfectly and on time, but save yourself some headaches and cash flow problems by budgeting for unforeseen delays.
- Have a savings cushion. In other words, if you are entirely supporting yourself, have at least three-to-six month's business and living expenses saved before you contemplate opening your office doors. Unlike other jobs, you will be unable to work if you suddenly become hurt or ill, so a little risk management planning is a necessity.
- Once you complete your business plan expenses and estimate your potential first-year income, you may find that you fall short in the way of profitability. Don't let this discourage you! Revisit your start-up expenses and see if there are any things you can live without at first. Fancy software, a high-end computer and plush sofa might be things you *want* for your office, but they are not necessities in building a successful practice. In your first year of business, the more you exclusively concentrate your funds, time and energy on getting and retaining clients, the more successful you will be. Keep in mind that very few businesses achieve profitability and great success right out of the gate, and if you need a cushion of savings or some supplemental income to sustain you initially, you are in good company with the vast majority of first-time entrepreneurs.

Next, it's time to explore your options when it comes to office space. There are a number of scenarios, some of which are described here:

## Office Sharing

Many therapists opt to rent office space that they share with other massage practitioners or complementary health practices, such as chiropractic, acupuncture, nutrition, etc. Office sharing provides a wonderful marketing opportunity to cross-refer to one another as well as the ability to pool resources for advertising, promotions and supplies.

Most massage therapists have no desire to work seven days per week, so another great option is to share an office with another massage therapist. You then split up the week or month between yourselves and share the rent accordingly. Another beneficial component of this scenario is that one of you can work with the other's clients while you are on vacation or taking time off. It is ideal if the two of you offer different, complementary but non-competing modalities.

Downsides of Office Sharing:

As with any partnership arrangement, issues are bound to come up. Try to have everything in writing from the outset, and list responsibilities and expectations. Make sure everyone is on the same page when it comes to providing service to your clients, especially if you will be sharing a receptionist or waiting area. Check references (really; do it!) when taking on a new officemate, and set an appropriate lease term. Don't forget to make sure that everyone in your office has the necessary liability and insurance coverage as a requirement for being part of your group. Most office share arrangements dictate that practitioners operate as completely independent businesses. However, if your group decides to form an association and practice under one group name, make sure that it is clear who legally owns the name of the business. For example, is it owned by the founder? Partners? Shared equally among members? Make sure it is determined *legally* and *in writing* as to what happens if one of the members decides to leave the group.

## Home Offices

Working from home is an excellent option in regard to your budget!

Not only will you save the expense of renting an outside office and commuting, you may also be able to deduct the expense of your home office from your income taxes. (Make sure that you note the dimensions of your home office and that the space is used solely for business purposes. More on deductions in Chapter 16.)

Downsides of a Home Office:

If you love being at home and working alone, this doesn't apply to you...
but some of us need to get outside the home and be around other people
to feel like we're "at work." Give some thought as to whether you might
fit into this category.

Clients tend to either love or hate home offices. Some enjoy the comfort
of going into someone's home, while others complain that "it feels like
going into someone's home." Go figure!

Home offices tend to inspire some degree of familiarity with clients,
so it is important to determine boundaries for yourself so people don't
assume it's alright to hang around afterward for a cup of tea. (That is,
unless you *want* them to hang around afterward for a cup of tea!) One
strategy that typically works is to gently let a dilly dallying client know
that you have another client arriving after them. This is a graceful way of
completing your time together as well as a sensitive reminder that you
are running a business and have other clients as well.

Be sure to review the licensing and zoning ordinances in your area to
make sure you can legally operate a home office. It may be a wise idea to
get to know your neighbors and familiarize them with massage therapy
so they understand what it is you do. Otherwise, if strangers are arriving
on your doorstep every hour or so, they may wonder exactly what is
going on in there. If parking is limited on your street, they may get bent
out of shape worrying that your guests will take up their parking spaces.
Instead of communicating their concern with you directly, many people
will call the police or other enforcement agencies. You can almost always
eliminate this occurrence by establishing good relationships with your
neighbors from the start.

Practice good safety habits when screening new clients. Always
remember that you are essentially inviting a stranger into your home,
and they will now know where you live. Word of mouth advertising
and marketing is best when conducting a home office practice and will
minimize the "stranger factor."

Finally, for better or for worse, maintaining a home office should inspire
you to keep a clean and organized home. Keep in mind that many
people have profound pet allergies or fears, so if you have dogs or cats
be sure to keep them outside of your massage room at all times. Some

individuals have allergies that are so pronounced that they can't even go to a therapist who has pets because they invariably wind up allergic to their sheets and towels. If you keep pets, it's a good idea to mention this to prospective clients when they're booking their first appointment.

## Outcall Massage

Outcall massage businesses are structured so that the therapist goes to the client's office, hotel or home. This is another great option to minimize your overhead as your office is essentially provided for you. Outcall-based massage businesses can be very lucrative, as clients expect to pay more for the convenience of the therapist coming to them. You may often build travel expenses, including tolls, parking and travel time into your rates. Many parents with small children appreciate having massage in their home, and when working with families you can often maximize your time and do two massages in a row within the same visit.

To be a successful outcall massage therapist, you will either need to possess (or learn) the twin arts of flexibility and spontaneity. When you have your own office space, or even a room within a spa, you are largely in control of your environment. Not so when you are in someone else's home! If you are a creature of habit and like to have everything in order, outcalls may not be for you. You should always expect the unexpected, but here are some tips and questions you should ask new clients in order to minimize surprises:

Parking: Do they have a driveway you can park in? Is there street parking? If street parking is difficult, is it possible to drop your table off once you arrive and then go find parking?

Animals: Do they have pets? Are they friendly?

Access: Are there a lot of steps or steep hills to negotiate? Occasionally clients will forget or not be aware that you will be bringing a rather large massage table and supplies with you. Make sure you'll be able to get your table in and out of their location with relative ease.

Music: I like to let clients know that I can bring special music for massage with me, or that they may listen to their own music. By letting them know ahead of time, clients will often already have the stereo set up and ready to go when I arrive.

One of the downsides of doing outcall massage is that you need to lug your table all over creation. You may wish to put the table on wheels or in a carrying case to make transporting it a little easier. Another challenge is driving and navigating new addresses, especially in the dark. Leave a little extra time for getting there, especially for new clients. When you have a new client, make note of the directions, actual driving time and the rate you charged them. This way, you don't have to ask them for the same information again when they rebook, and allows you to alter the rate if necessary (for example, if you had to pay for a parking garage or other unexpected expenses.)

Many outcall therapists complement their practices with chair massage work at corporations, special events or holiday parties. This type of work is typically very social and fun, as people are more likely to chat during these shortened sessions. Chair massage is an excellent way to generate income while you market your practice at the same time; many of your chair clients will book you independently for a table session. Occasionally a company will hire you to be on-site, but each client will be responsible for paying you directly. If the company gives you a choice, I recommend asking the company to pay you directly on an hourly basis. This way, you will be paid for your time regardless of whether or not you are fully booked. You may wish to carry along some promotional flyers and business cards to hand out during your chair massage work to further incent customers to contact you in the future. Better yet, have clients print their name, email address and telephone number on your mailing list so that you may contact them!

## Leasing Your Own Office Space

Having your own office gives you the ability to do whatever you choose! (Well, within the bounds of taste and landlord approval, of course.) You get to set your own hours, decorate the office and walls however you choose, and pick your own supplies and furniture.

When choosing an office space, pay attention to whom your neighbors will be and what kind of hours they keep. You certainly don't want to wind up locating next to an auto body shop or junior high school, so ask around! Office spaces located next to convenience shops, liquor stores, noisy hair salons, fast food or check cashing facilities are generally not good choices. For example, you don't want your clients smelling chemical perm treatments or fried chicken while they're trying to relax. Once you've got your eye on a particular space, visit it at different days and times. One therapist I know leased an office space next to a very serene, picturesque park. What she didn't realize, however, was that the same quiet, lovely park became a skateboarding destination during after-school and weekend hours (the "prime time" hours for massage appointments.) She - and her clients - were stuck listening to the sound of yelling adolescents and grating wheels for the six months of her lease. Not so relaxing! Once you find a space you like, perform a sight-smell-hearing test at the location during different times of day and evening. Put yourself in the shoes of your client and take note of what they will be looking at, smelling, and hearing when they enter, exit and during their session.

Safe, accessible and convenient parking is universally important to clients. Make sure that there is appropriate and adequate parking available for them. Observe the parking availability during the evening and make sure it is well-lit. If your office space only allows for one or two cars, by all means leave the spaces open for your clients and find another place to keep your own car nearby.

Before you sign a lease, make sure your location will meet all zoning requirements in your city or county. Or, you can make your lease conditional on clearing zoning regulations and receiving permits, if necessary. Zoning law is designed to restrict and control what kinds of businesses can operate in different neighborhoods, so it is vital that you are permitted to practice massage in your chosen location. Once you receive permission, get it in writing and store it in a safe place.

Take some time to introduce yourself to your new neighbors just in case they have any misconceptions about massage therapy. If they are unfamiliar, you may wish to invite them to visit for an introductory offer or give them some brochures and information.

Have a few friends or family members come to receive a massage at your new office and pretend as if they are a first time client. Ask them to give you an unbiased review as to temperature, décor, noise, comfort level and any advice they have. For instance, you may adore a room full of the scent of patchouli, while others would greet that as a waking nightmare. Be sensitive when burning sage or incense. Strive to create an environment that will provide broad appeal to the general public; it is better to err on the side of neutrality than be offensive. The vast majority of clients will never speak up or give you constructive criticism unless you specifically ask for it. Give your clients the opportunity to express themselves openly every once in awhile by asking them directly or in the form of a customer survey.

Don't forget to pick up some business property insurance in addition to the standard liability policy for massage therapists. Your professional massage association may offer property insurance (see Chapter 4 for more information.) It is relatively inexpensive and valuable to have in case anything gets stolen or broken in your office. (Some policies will even cover your business property if it is in your automobile or at another location; check it out!)

One of your more significant investments in a new office will be your massage table. Spend some time researching the different brands online or at your local massage supply store. While you're shopping, ask yourself the following questions:

- Will you be traveling with your table often, once in awhile or will it remain exclusively in your office space? How portable and lightweight does your table need to be?
- Will other practitioners be using your table (and adjusting it) as well? How simple is it to adjust?
- Does the table have a store or manufacturer warranty? Return policy?
- If the table breaks, what is the process of repairing or replacing it? Will there be any out-of-pocket expenses for you?

Practice opening a table, setting it up, adjusting its height, carrying it around and closing it. Don't forget to test it by laying on it! How does it feel? Pay special attention to the face cradle; a comfortable face cradle can make a world of difference to your client's experience of your massage. Try to find one that is comfortable and highly adjustable.

When ordering a table and other supplies, I strongly encourage you to touch, feel and test them out whenever possible, especially the expensive items that you will be using for a long time. If chosen wisely and taken good care of, you will be able to use your table, face cradle, sheets, pillows and bolsters for many years.

When setting up your office and hours, try to put yourself in the place of your client. Arrange furniture in a logical way, and provide some privacy for them to dress/undress. If your office is only one room, a folding shoji screen of some kind works nicely. Have a comfortable place for clients to sit and wait if they are early, as well as a place to recover afterward (and before they try to drive). Little things like fresh water, some fruit or nuts, and light reading are thoughtful things to provide for your clients. If you do not have a shower facility, keep some extra towels on hand for them to wipe excess lotion or oil off after their massage. Try to use non-staining and non-greasy lotion, oil or creams for those clients that need to return to work. Dimmer switches on lamps and volume controls for stereos can accommodate a variety of customer preferences. You may wish to keep a small decorative bowl or dish on a stand directly next to the massage table for clients to store their jewelry or watch during their session.

There is no need to go overboard on spending to decorate your office, especially when you are just starting out. Focus your budget on attracting new clients, improving your skills and marketing your practice. Clients often pay less attention to décor than you may realize. Remember, for most of their visit, the room is darkened and the client is either facedown or has their eyes closed!

Likewise, it is typically unnecessary at the outset to invest in complex software programs and high-powered computers to manage your clientele. Instead, focus on building client relationships. Later, when you have a multitude of clients or have grown into a larger organization, your technology and streamlining operations will become a more timely issue.

# CHAPTER 8

## ESTABLISHING A PRIVATE PRACTICE

One strategy you may wish to consider when branching out on your own is to work a few days per week at your employer and dedicate the other days to working with clients in your private practice. Then, as you build your business you will eventually reach critical mass and have enough clients to leave your "day job."

Whatever you do, don't open your own office and suddenly quit your job in a blaze of glory, or fury for that matter! Even if you're the most highly skilled practitioner around and can't stand your boss or manager, be professional. Give the requisite notice (usually two weeks), be discreet, and resist the urge to trash talk your former place of employment. Quietly inform your loyal clients that you will be leaving over the next few weeks, but that they are welcome to come see you at your new office. Do not actively recruit or try to "steal" clients from your employer.

I can't tell you how many times I've seen therapists walk off the job with little or no notice, assuming that their clientele would flock to their new office and business would simply boom from the start. Many of these therapists were the spa's 'superstars' and perennially booked solid. Oh, how wrong they were. Remember, excellent skills are only one piece of building a successful practice, and you must cultivate all the necessary components to build a truly great one. In many cases, these therapists were ultimately forced to crawl back nine months later to ask if they could have their old job back...and eat some serious crow. Don't be this therapist! Always be humble, professional, respectful and try your best to stay on good terms with everyone in the industry. Over time, it will come to repay you in spades.

### Transitioning from Employee to Independent Practitioner

If you are leaving your former workplace and opening an office in the same community, you may already have a client list and following. Don't take them for granted! Reach out to everyone and offer them a promotion to come see you at your new office. One of the most significant shifts you must make once you establish your own practice is to move from a passive/receptive state to one of actionable steps when it comes to marketing and promoting yourself.

Many human beings are creatures of habit, and once we get used to getting our massages in a certain place we need to be motivated to go someplace new. For example, the spa where you used to work may have posh locker facilities, free brownies and a sauna for guest use. Sure, your spa customers adore you and love your work, but they also may love the customer service or amenities provided at your former location. Realize that clients might be giving certain things up when they come to see you, so be aware of that and try to provide little extras to help them overcome their resistance. A free product sample, a complimentary head massage add-on for fifteen minutes... any incentives you can come up with that will be valuable to your clientele and make them feel special.

## Naming Your Practice

While many therapists choose to operate their business under their own name, others prefer to use a fictitious business name to make it clear they are offering massage therapy services. When you are choosing a name, take care not to be too narrow or limiting in scope. For example, you may currently live in Smallsville and think that Smallsville Massage Therapy has a nice ring to it. But, one – you may move, and then lose all the branding and goodwill you've created attached to that name, and two – you may expand into other cities and wish you had chosen a name with wider applicability.

Once you've chosen a potential name, perform an internet search to see who else may be already using that business name. Also, visit the United States Patent and Trademark website (uspto.gov) and run a trademark search on the name. If someone has already trademarked a similar name, you should carefully think it over before going ahead and using it. Using a previously trademarked name, you run the risk of ultimately receiving a cease and desist order if the owner feels you are operating in violation of his/her trademark. If everything looks good after searching, you may wish to file your own trademark to protect your name. Trademark lawyers can accomplish this for you, or you can follow the instructions at the USPTO website and file it on your own.

Even if you don't plan on creating a website for your business right away, it is a good idea to reserve and purchase the domain name (or

URL) that matches your business. For example, if your business name is Tina Peters Massage Therapy, you may reserve www.tinapeters.com. Reserving a domain name is very inexpensive, and is only a nominal fee to renew each year. Once you reserve a name, you own it for a specified period of time, during which the name is protected from use by other parties. Since the cost is relatively low, it is well worth reserving your business name even if you don't necessarily plan on having a website right away.

## Booking Appointments

For many therapists, this may be the first time you are booking your own appointments and interacting with clients on the phone. Pay attention to your telephone etiquette and manner, and ask for feedback from some trusted clients if you're not sure how you are coming across on the phone. Similarly, if you use email to set appointments and keep in touch with clients, be sure to use proper grammar, spelling and a professional tone.

Set goals in order to keep yourself focused and moving forward. For instance, resolve to gain five new clients this month, and then take manageable steps toward that goal by actively handing out your business cards, striking up more massage-related conversations and posting flyers at targeted locations. Make a commitment to yourself and your practice— a little bit of effort each day, spread out over time, will build the most loyal and consistent clientele.

From the outset, carry yourself as a professional and allow professional ideals to guide the way you speak, dress and interact with clients. Likewise, treat your business as a business, not a hobby. Once you embark in a private practice you will be responsible for many facets of business that may be brand new to you. Pick up some books or enroll in some basic business classes in marketing and promotion if this is an area you need help with. Especially in the beginning, these business activities may vastly outweigh the hands-on time you spend with clients.

Unless you are in session, make every effort to answer client calls rather than allowing them to go to voicemail. In our instant gratification culture, by the time you return their call they may have found something else to do. For many clients, massage is not something they receive regularly but instead call out of desperation or spur of the moment. These clients will most likely take the first appointment they can get, so make answering your phone a top priority.

Your telephone manner should reflect that of your client, and you can adjust it accordingly. With busy executives, you should be focused, precise and straight to the point. If a client has more time, feel free to be more relaxed and easy-going in your tone. But always – no matter who the client is – try to book the appointment while you have them on the phone the first time. This isn't always possible, but making a point of trying will give you better odds of it happening.

Smile when you answer the phone, and sound genuinely happy to hear from a client. Choose a calendar or appointment book that you can readily keep with you at all times. Try to have it nearby when you take a client call, or engage them in friendly conversation for a moment while you track it down. Eliminate background noise, including barking dogs, screaming children or blasting stereos while you're on the phone with clients, and preferably before you even answer. If your work and personal phone are one and the same, assume each call is a business call and state your name rather than a casual hello.

Your voicemail should be professional-sounding, clear and without background music or noise. The message should affirm that the caller has found the right person (i.e. it should be in your voice and mention your name) but not go on too long. All of us have at least one friend with an impossible voicemail greeting… one that subjects you to a song, a too-lengthy greeting or a phone that rings so long that by the time you get to the voicemail you've forgotten who or why you called! Make certain your voicemail allows long messages to be left by your clients. They may wish to leave you a list of optional days and times for appointments, directions to their home or other lengthy information. It can be frustrating to record a long message only to be cut off and have to re-record the entire thing. Work with your phone company to make sure your voicemail allotment is as long as possible.

Return voicemails promptly, and be discreet if anyone other than your client answers the telephone. If you must leave a message with a secretary or family member, it is fine to simply leave your name and mention you are returning their call.

## Setting Your Office Hours

Keep in mind that the office hours you set will influence the type of clientele you draw. For example, if you wish to keep "regular" business hours, i.e. 9-5, Monday through Friday, you will largely limit yourself to stay-at-home parents, self-employed people with flexible schedules, and retired individuals. If you opt to work occasional evenings and weekends, you will attract a greater variety of clients and more professionals who are only free during those hours.

Consider if you are a "morning person," or a "night person." Massage is a very physically demanding profession, and it's ideal if you can work in confluence with your energetic peak times. For example, I'm a night person, so I greatly prefer to work between 3pm and 10pm. My clients love the fact that I'm available to them after work, before dinner, or late evening just before bedtime, and I enjoy working when my energy is at its strongest. Do I occasionally work in the morning to accommodate a client? Sure. But I notice a big difference in how I feel during the session and how quickly my body recovers. In time you will figure out what works best for you and your body and adjust your office hours accordingly.

I recommend not posting firm operating hours for your practice until you have been in business for some time and feel fairly certain they will not change. You don't want to spend money posting your hours on expensive signage, brochures or a website only to have them change. As you grow and establish your practice, you will learn how many massage sessions you can comfortably perform in a day or week. This number will vary from therapist to therapist, and might vary over time depending on what else is going on in your life. I know therapists who can work a 9-5 day, doing eight massages in a row, nearly nonstop. Others prefer to do two or three sessions in a day at the most. The key to setting your hours and optimizing your practice over the long-term is listening to your body.

## The Intake Form

Creating an intake form for first-time clients is a wonderful way to get to know valuable information about them, inform them of your business policies and ascertain their initial motivation for coming in. If you have room in your schedule, I suggest offering a complimentary intake interview for all new clients. This can be as simple as asking them to come in a half hour early for their first session. During this time they can fill out the forms and still have fifteen to twenty minutes to chat with you. An intake interview is time well spent; it establishes personal rapport, communication and sets the tone for ongoing care. Have clients sign and date the intake form, and keep it in your files for future reference.

Information to include on the intake form:
- Name
- Contact Information – Phone numbers, email address, mailing address
- Reason they are coming in for massage – relaxation, in pain, stress, injury, etc.
- How they heard about you – Who were they referred by?
- Emergency contact person and information
- Their birth date
- Special concerns – Recent illnesses, physical or emotional trauma, injuries, surgeries, etc.
- Have they had a massage before? Frequency?
- Are they pregnant or trying to become pregnant?
- Are they on any medications?
- Allergies or sensitivities?
- Do they wear contacts or eyeglasses?
- Can you add them to your mailing list?
- Cancellation policy
- Bounced check policy
- Payment expectations – At the time of service; credit cards accepted
- Notification that your massage is strictly therapeutic and non-sexual in nature
- Their goals in receiving massage? Stress reduction, relaxation, to get out of pain, etc.
- Statement that you are not responsible for personal items that are lost or left behind
- Statement of confidentiality

Include a line where the client may sign and date the intake form to signify they have read and acknowledged your terms and policies. Formulate an easily accessible client record system where you can keep intake forms and notes from your sessions. If you practice a lot of outcall massage, you may also wish to keep directions to the client's home as well as the rate you charged them. If you only see a client infrequently, it is understandable that you may not remember their last name. For this reason, you may wish to file client records in alphabetical order by first name. It's also a great idea to keep client phone numbers stored in multiple places in the event one source gets lost (you drop your mobile phone in the sink, your computer crashes, etc.)

# Pricing Your Services

Many massage therapists either struggle initially with what to charge for their work or have issues communicating with clients when it comes to quoting their rates. One remedy to this is to have a variety of services and prices. For example, you may offer sessions from thirty minutes to two hours in length, and when someone inquires what you charge, you can reply, "My rates start at $45" (for the thirty minute session.) Rest assured, the longer you practice the more confident and comfortable you will grow with expressing yourself when it comes to your rates.

Make sure your prices are in alignment with the going rate in your area, especially when you are just starting out. According to the American Massage Therapy Association, its member therapists charge an average of $63 per hour, and overall earn an average hourly wage of $41.50. Take care not to under or overprice your services. Your rates should be clearly posted and kept consistent among your clients; clients will be understandably upset if they discover one day that they have been charged more than someone else for the same service.

Unlike some other professions, we cannot usually charge more for complex or challenging cases. One way many therapists add charges gracefully is by setting a higher price for "deep tissue" or "specialty massage" in the hopes that larger and more muscular clients will opt for these sessions. I did come across one therapist who charged "by the pound" (no kidding); he would place each client on a scale before their session began. I generally do not recommend this manner of pricing if you ever hope to have any female clients!

Although many practitioners use the model, I also don't recommend offering a sliding-scale except in special circumstances or for a pre-existing client you know very well. (For example, a long term client has just been laid off from their job. Instead of losing their business altogether, you may opt to offer them a sliding scale rate based on what they can afford to pay until they find work again.) When it comes to sliding scales, people at lower income levels often feel guilty and pay more than they should, while those in the highest income brackets are often the most frugal and will underpay if given the choice.

When it comes time to raise your rates, give your clients plenty of notice and possibly some incentives or add-ons to off-set any 'sticker shock.' I recommend sending out a thoughtfully written note to clients letting them know that your rates will go up as of a particular date (thirty to ninety days from the date you send the letter is a good amount of notice.) In the notice, don't forget to include a statement of gratitude and appreciation of their support of your practice. (Many times these notes will have the happy side-effect of clients rushing to book with you before the price increase, so be prepared and make room in your schedule!)

Practice stating your rates without hesitation or pause, in a tone that is warm, direct and confident. Often in life, we must ask for what we deserve rather than wait for someone else to speak up for us. When I was a new therapist I was working at a spa for nearly a year before I discovered a recent hire was making several dollars more per hour than I was, even though I had been there much longer. I only found out when I was accidentally given his paycheck, and saw that it was much bigger than mine! After I approached the owner, he quickly raised my pay to match it. When I asked why the other therapist had been paid more, the owner's answer was simple: he asked. This episode taught me a valuable lesson. Stand up for yourself and make sure you are being paid what you are worth and on par with others in your organization.

Most therapists begin doing massage as a second career (82% according to the AMTA), so if you need to supplement your income with a primary or second job while you're building your practice you are not alone. In 2008, the average massage therapist earned $31,500 in income; if this figure is much lower than the standard of living you are accustomed to, you will need to make adjustments or rely on savings for awhile.

## "Re-Branding" Yourself

In many instances, our first clients as newly independent massage therapists are people we already know, such as our family, friends and acquaintances. If you have been in a different industry for some time, your circle may identify you with your former job and have trouble making the mental shift to thinking of you as a massage therapist, first. If this sounds like you, you will need to take active steps to "re-invent" yourself. Here are some tips to help establish your new identity as a massage therapist:

- Be open and ask for help! Let your friends and family know that you are actively trying to establish yourself and your practice and that you need their help in getting the word out. Give everyone you know some business cards and encourage them to hand them out.

- Expand your circle. Get out and meet new people, introducing yourself as a massage therapist.
- Take up new activities and hobbies that will allow you to meet new people.
- Wear 'massage therapist' shirts and clothing. While this may sound silly, whenever I wear my tee shirts that have my business logo on them, I find strangers notice and strike up a conversation to inquire about massage.

## Retaining Clients

Once you have a stable of regular clients one of the biggest mistakes you can make is not staying in touch with them. Often the only difference between booking a session and not booking a session is a simple phone call or email reminding them of your existence! Many therapists focus much of their budget and time on marketing for new clients to the detriment of their existing clientele. The more energy and resources you put into retaining clients, the less you have to put into advertising for new ones. Alongside your marketing and promotional efforts, remember to continue to lavish attention on the clients you already have.

Many people are so busy these days that they enjoy keeping a "standing appointment" on a designated day and time each week. Introduce the idea to those clients who you think this arrangement might work well, and offer them an advanced booking discount or other incentive. While it is ideal to rebook clients immediately following an appointment with you, it is not always practical for people with unpredictable schedules, demanding jobs or ever-changing family responsibilities. Be understanding if someone initially declines your offer to rebook; you can always touch base with them in a couple weeks by telephone or email just to check in, see how they are doing and ask if they'd like to make another appointment. Make a point of keeping in regular contact with your customers, and practice doing little things to make them feel appreciated. Don't wait until your rent is due to start calling clients!

Self-promotion and sales are typically not the forte of massage therapists, so don't think of your outreach in those terms. Perhaps you saw something that reminded you of a client, or you have information to share with them, or you just wish to see how they're feeling. This way, you're not calling them specifically to book a session, but odds are they will anyway.

When you have a new client, have them add their birthday to the initial intake form. Remember your clients on their birthdays, holidays and when you know they have a special event coming up, such as a wedding or anniversary. Remember them, too, if there is an illness or death in their family. Take the time to send them a thank you card if they've referred a new client to you.

I recommend keeping a small supply of various cards on hand, especially birthday and thank you cards, so you can mail them right away as the opportunity arises.

There are some fantastic email marketing programs out there that make it a snap to create professional newsletters. For a small monthly fee, you can maintain your client contact list online and stay in touch through monthly or quarterly newsletters. Just make sure you get permission to add your client's name to your list. An easy way to do this is to have them check a box to be added to your mailing list on their initial intake form, or through a sign-up box on your website, if you have one.

Word of mouth is an outstanding way to build your client base, but it takes time. Take advantage of any opportunity to thank clients that have referred you to others. Remembering and expressing gratitude for a client's thoughtfulness is an excellent way to ensure they remain your client!

Another way to retain clients is to offer a discounted series of sessions that they pay for up front. For example, a client gets six massages for the price of five, or "buy five and get the sixth free." This is a great way to generate cash flow, but keep in mind not to do too many of these or you will wind up feeling like you're working for free in a few months.

Around the holidays, I like to offer my regular clients a "buy one get a free gift certificate" promotion. During the holidays, people tend to get overwhelmed and stressed out, as well as less likely to take the time to get a massage for themselves (just when they need it most!) This promotion enables them to get a massage, plus get a gift for a loved one at the same time.

Every once in awhile, analyze each client's individual value to your practice. That is, the amount of income each of your regular, long term clients provides over time. For example, you may see one client once every other week all year long. Another client may only see you once per month year-round, but they may refer ten new clients to you in that same time period. This exercise will illuminate the contribution each client makes in terms of loyalty and referrals. Once you clearly see, on paper, exactly how much a weekly or bi-weekly client means to your practice over the course of a year, you will find a whole new level of appreciation for them. Take a few moments during each year to remember and appreciate them for supporting your business.

Practice amazing customer service. After your session is complete, take notes on your client's body as well as some key things you discussed so you can later jog your memory. During their next session, when you remember to inquire how their anniversary was or how their daughter's wedding went, they will feel listened to and appreciated. Allow your client to be the star and center of attention during your time together.

# CHAPTER 9

## MAINTAINING YOUR PRACTICE

### Avoiding Burn-Out

As massage therapists, there are several types of burn-out we need to watch out for: physical, mental and emotional.

When you're first starting out in your practice, it is likely that your hands, fingers and arms aren't accustomed to being used that much and in quite that way. Some initial soreness is natural. Take care to minimize the use of your fingers, and instead use your forearms and elbows as a substitute. Keep your wrists as straight as possible. Work from your core and keep it strong through regular exercise. Your massage school may offer a class in proper body mechanics, or ask your teacher to analyze your movement so you know what maintaining good posture feels like.

Take care not to work too many hours and set reasonable goals for yourself. Remember, performing 15-25 massage sessions each week is considered full-time. According to AMTA statistics, its members average giving 19 hours of massage per week, and 41 massages per month.

It will take some time for your body to adjust to the demands of performing massage therapy on a regular basis. Give yourself some extra TLC while you are building up your strength. When I first started doing massage therapy, I treated my body as if I was training for an athletic event – lots of rest, ice and hot baths! There are a few parts of the anatomy that bear the brunt of the action when doing massage; be sure to take extra special care of the following potential trouble spots:

Wrists: Especially if you have a smaller body frame, putting pressure on the wrists can cause problems over time. Take care to keep your wrists as straight as possible, especially when lifting a heavier client's legs, arms or head. You have no idea how heavy a human head is until you hold it in your hands!

Fingers/finger joints: The fingers and joints can become inflamed from overuse. If this happens, try to use them less, ice them at the end of your

day, and remove inflammatory foods (such as the nightshade family…
eggplant, nicotine, tomatoes) from your diet temporarily. Try to cut
down on sugar and increase your water intake. Acupuncture and/or an
occasional ibuprofen may also give you some relief.

Low back and neck: The back or neck of a massage therapist may get
sore from all the bent over postures and repetitive motions that we do.
Make sure your massage table is at its ideal height so as not to stress your
back. If you travel with your massage table often, you may wish to put
it on wheels. Practice corrective stretches or yoga poses to "open" the
back and chest after so much bending over. Build a strong core through
abdominal exercises and draw on that strength while giving massage.

## Overcoming Plateaus

According to statistics, the average massage therapist stays in the field,
performing massage, for 6.3 years. After practicing for a year or two,
most massage therapists have learned to work in a way that keeps them
physically safe from overuse and physical injuries. In the years that
follow, however, you may go through a phase I refer to as The Plateau, a
period of time where you may feel mentally bored, restless or tired of
doing massage. Not everyone will go through this, but if you do, please
realize it's completely normal!

Some things you can do to help get you through and over your plateau are:

- Take a class or workshop in massage or in a complementary
  practice. Learning new skills and meeting new people may give
  your practice the creative spark you need.

- Travel. Take a trip if you can, or switch things up in your office.
  Rearrange furnishings, get some new prints for the walls, or
  bring some plants or fish in.

- Check in with yourself. How is your home and personal life?
  Our profession is a very giving one, and it is important that we
  have a support system and people around who care about us to
  keep things in balance. Get rid of the energy leeches in your
  life (the negative people who drain your energy) and seek out
  positive, productive people and relationships.

- Tap into your creative energy. Sometimes, for all sorts
  of reasons, our energy can become stuck. For long-time

practitioners, massage therapy is usually a strong channel of consistent, creative outlet and expression. So it's a problem when it gets stuck, especially when it is our profession! Think of writer's block; it's very similar. Tap back into that creative energy by a different means if necessary. Start a journaling practice. Paint. Sculpt. Read, or view beautiful art… anything that appeals to you, really. Sometimes just giving the energy a different means of expression is enough to do the trick.

## Staying Healthy

Diet and nutrition are vitally important when you rely on your body for your work. A nutritious, wholesome diet will keep your energy levels up and allow you to perform a physically demanding job like massage therapy for many years. Pay extra attention that you are getting the protein, vitamins and iron your body needs, and supplement your diet if necessary.

Getting regular exercise keeps you healthy, physically fit, gets your energy moving and helps shake off the stresses of the day. It also helps to dissipate any energy you may have picked up from your clients. Choose whatever form of exercise you most enjoy. Hiking, dancing, running, cycling, and swimming are all great choices. Incorporate a stretching practice into your daily routine to counteract the tension created by performing massage. There is no one perfect prescription for everyone when it comes to exercise – some people require very vigorous work-outs while others thrive on gentle hikes. The most important thing is to choose something you enjoy and that makes you feel good and balanced.

Personally speaking, I would be lost without my yoga practice! Yoga helps me put everything back into alignment, physically re-opening my neck, chest, back and shoulders and restoring my energy. There are countless styles of yoga to study – from very gentle to extremely demanding - and you may want to sample a number of types before finding the perfect modality for you. I also rely on meditation, walking in nature, and reading books on spirituality and growth to stay in balance. Don't be afraid to try a variety of things until you find the right combination for you. The more you expose yourself to alternative healing practices the better informed you will be, which will ultimately benefit both you and your clients.

Warm, Epsom salt baths are an excellent way to wind down the day and prepare your body for rest. The salts assist the body in detoxification

from daily stress, client energies, as well as environmental toxins
and pollution. If you don't have a bathtub, a warm footbath can be an
effective and soothing substitute.

Treat your hands like the treasured possessions they are! For the sake of
your clients as well as yourself, keep your hands moisturized and soft
with short nails and healthy cuticles. If you are leaving scratch marks on
your client's back, that is a clear sign that your nails should be trimmed.
Treat your hands and fingers to a regular manicure to keep them soft
and healthy.

Avoid injury. Practice conscious body mechanics and remember to use
your whole body when lifting or moving heavy limbs. If you already have
an inkling that you're accident-prone, you may want to avoid activities
that may injure your hands, wrists or arms in an accident. For example,
I tend to avoid bicycling at all costs since I'm a well-established klutz
when it comes to this activity. Some occupations allow for a broken arm
or leg; massage therapy is unfortunately not so forgiving!

Maintain healthy boundaries. Massage therapy is very personal work, and
it is natural to become close with your clients. Likewise, many therapists
will regularly work on friends and family. Therefore, it is very important
to set good boundaries when you have a social relationship with clients,
and continue to respect their privacy and confidentiality as you would
any other client. If friends or family members are asking you to work on
them a little too often, you may need to ask them to book time with you
during your regular hours. Keep your relationships in balance.

Get regular massage! Receiving bodywork is imperative to our physical
and mental health as well as continued growth and learning. Many
therapists find a partner practitioner to trade sessions; one week one
therapist receives a session, and the next week they trade places. Book
one another just as you would a paying client so you can each feel like
it's a "real" massage, fully enjoy the experience and maximize its benefits.
Trading or going to different therapists is also a fantastic way to learn
new modalities, stretches and a time to be 'in the shoes' of your clients.

Take time off. Try to schedule regular days off, ideally consecutive days to
give your body more time to rest and rejuvenate. A few times per year, try
to take one week or more off when you give no massage or bodywork.

   *When taking one week or more off, you may wonder what to
   do with your clients who see you on a weekly basis. Give your

clients as much notice as possible so that they may schedule a session right before you leave. Once clients receive a message letting them know you will be away, many will book a session, even if they had previously not thought of doing so. Just a little prompt will suffice!

While you're away, change your work voicemail to state that you are currently out of the office and mention the date you will be returning. If you will retain phone access while you're away, you may say in the recording that you'll be checking messages regularly and scheduling appointments. Ask them to please leave their desired day and time for their appointment. This way you can just return their call and confirm the appointment in just a few short minutes.

If you're going to be away longer than one week, it is thoughtful to leave the name and number of a fellow massage therapist to refer to. Many clients will enjoy trying someone new and appreciate having someone you like and trust to see until you return. Hopefully your colleague will return the favor the next time he/she goes on vacation!

# CHAPTER 10

## THE PRACTITIONER-CLIENT RELATIONSHIP

One of the most valuable lessons you will learn over the course of a long-term practice is the understanding that your clients are coming to you for many different reasons, reasons that may change over the course of months or years. Whether emotional, physical or spiritual, massage therapy has the ability to fulfill a surprising number of human needs. Some individuals may come for connection and conversation while others seek out massage for a calming, silent sanctuary. The key is being able to recognize and honor the uniqueness of each client and then adapt your approach accordingly. Having a basic understanding of human nature will help you appreciate the individual and very personal motivations of your clients, deepening your ability to work with each of them. We all want to feel a sense of belonging and acknowledgement; take every opportunity you have to appreciate your clients.

If you ask most of my clients to tell you about me, most of them would say that I am unfailingly cheerful, positive and encouraging. I greet clients as if it is Christmas morning and I am thrilled to see them, and the truth is, I usually am. Am I like this every day in my real life? Certainly not! But I make certain that during sessions my number one focus is on my client and their experience of our time together. I want them to feel better physically when they leave, but I also want them to feel lighter, more peaceful, happier and uplifted. Clients will come to you initially for your skills alone, but they will stay with you for the long haul if you make it a point to make them feel special on every level.

### Notes on Transference

An unfortunate yet common side effect of being an empathic, intuitive and sensitive human being – qualities that are ideal for a massage therapist – is transference. Transference occurs when we pick up the subtle energies and feelings of our clients, and it's very common when we are a new therapist just starting out.

Transference can manifest in many ways, some obvious and some not-so-obvious. For example, when I was brand new to massage, if I had a client come in with a headache, it was common for them to leave without the headache, but it would reappear in *my* head. This is an obvious example of transference, but more often you will just sense a shift in your mood or feelings. These shifts can range from anger, to sadness, to just plain feeling lousy. Transference is tricky because occasionally it is hard to tell whether it is our own feelings surfacing, or if we are taking on the feelings of our clients. In either case, the goal is to acknowledge any negative energy that arises so it may be released in a safe and harmless manner.

## Limiting Transference

You can limit transference by maintaining clear, balanced energetic boundaries between yourself and your clients. Keep your own energy strong with practices such as yoga, Tai Chi, Qigong, meditation or deep breathing exercises. During your session, imagine yourself surrounded by a healing, protective white light (or any similar visual that resonates with you.) At the end of the day, rinse client energies away with a bath or shower, aromatherapy, or some relaxed stretching. After each session, rub your hands together under cool, running water and visualize the energetic residue washing away.

Since you can't always entirely eliminate transference, try to use it when it appears in your practice. Transferred feelings often appear as an unexpressed or unconscious emotion in a client, so it may assist your intuition in deciding what kind of bodywork they need most. Instead of viewing it as something to avoid at all costs, you can choose to see it as the client's subconscious way of providing a little hint.

## Client Challenges

### Late Clients

One challenge commonly voiced by massage therapists is dealing with clients who are perpetually late. One tactic you may use is inserting a "cushion," or extra time, around that particular client's appointment. This will allow you to accommodate their lateness, still give them their full treatment time, plus avoid inconveniencing your next client.

Another way to deal with this issue is to only give the late client the amount of time remaining in their session. This is the option most often used by spas and resorts. For example, if a client is 15 minutes late for his/her one hour massage, he/she will only receive 45 minutes of treatment time. Employing this method, you should be prepared to deal with an angry client occasionally. But if you stand your ground your clients will quickly learn to respect your time as they would any other professional. The longer you're in practice and the more established your clientele, the freer you may feel in setting firm boundaries. If you're just starting out in business, you may want to be a little more flexible at the outset.

## LAST-MINUTE BOOKINGS & CANCELLATIONS

Some people are planners and like to have their weekly schedules all lined up in advance. These types of clients are a dream come true for massage therapists as they provide consistency and predictability to your practice and income. However, many individuals are more spontaneous or tend to seek massage once they're already in some degree of discomfort. You can certainly encourage your clients to book in advance, however if you also welcome clients who call for same day appointments you will definitely increase your client base. Try not to get frustrated by last minute calls; it's only human nature!

Clients who are in the habit of not showing up for scheduled appointments are another matter. Make sure all clients know your policy when it comes to cancellations and rescheduling. Include your cancellation policy on the intake form that all new clients fill out and sign. This way you have it in writing that they were aware of the penalty for canceling last minute or not showing up for their scheduled appointment.

Use your judgment here; all of us have the ability to occasionally space out and completely forget about an appointment. Therefore, you may want to cut a client some slack if they have an emergency come up or they accidentally forget. It's often not worth risking a long term client relationship over a single incident. You will definitely minimize no-shows by confirming appointments a day ahead. After getting their permission, I suggest using email or text messaging to confirm clients rather than telephoning them. It's a quick, easy way to confirm without interrupting their day or evening.

## MANAGING EXPECTATIONS

In the course of a massage career, you will experience many occasions when you will be able to successfully clear up a client's presenting issue in just one session. However, it is much more common to require multiple sessions and consistent work over time. When a client presents you with a specific issue, it is vital that you communicate with them and manage their expectations.

Some clients will expect to show up once and have you fix whatever ailment or discomfort they are having. Athletes are especially notorious in this regard. There are few things an athlete likes to hear less than being told they need to rest, so they often arrive desperate for you to "fix them" so they can get back to their training immediately. You will also run across a fair amount of middle-aged clients who present you with injuries they attained in high school or accidents that occurred twenty years ago. Others will expect you to clear up aches and pains in the course of a sixty minute session that have accrued over decades.

To manage expectations, get clients to talk about what they expect from your time together during the intake process. Listen carefully, acknowledge them, and use your response to gently educate the client if they are expecting a miracle. For example, you may need to explain that it can take time to re-train the body and musculature, especially if an injury was incurred long ago. It is often necessary, too, to educate clients on the interconnectedness of the human body. Someone may come to you complaining of lower back pain, for instance, and you may discover the root of the problem is their exceptionally tight hamstrings. Now, if they complain of back pain, and you silently focus on their legs, they may think you're ignoring their needs. In these instances it is very important to explain what you're doing and why you're doing it. Communication is key. Utilize learning tools such as anatomical charts and muscle models to show clients exactly where their pain is coming from. Sometimes a good visual really makes a difference!

### Client Complaints

If you practice massage for any length of time, you will undoubtedly have a client complain about you or your work at some point. So, it's best to know at the outset that even the very best therapists out there have dealt with a challenging client or two!

It is an unfortunate part of human nature that we sometimes take out our stress and frustration on unsuspecting recipients. This will unfailingly occur in any service type work you could possibly choose. Occasionally you may have a client who just needs to vent or complain... about anything! A person in this frame of mind will look for any excuse or problem, so don't take it personally. One massage therapist I know uses a tactic she calls "killing them with kindness." She can turn the most terrible mood or rant into serenity by blanketing her client with humor, compliments and kindness. You can overcome almost any client's negativity by allowing them to feel heard while balancing the mood with positive energy. And when all else fails, remember you only have to see this person for an hour. Keep your cool, stay professional and be thankful you're not related. (Assuming you're not!)

Many instances of complaints can be resolved by practicing open communication. Try to make your clients feel like they can express themselves during the session so that you can make appropriate adjustments *before* a problem occurs. Allow an upset client to feel heard and don't discount or minimize their feelings, even if they appear to be bent out of shape over something rather silly. Try to sympathize as best you can while gracefully re-focusing their attention on their body.

A common occurrence with clients new to massage is feeling pain or soreness after a session, especially the next day. Often this is a combination of the client's musculature not being accustomed to massage therapy and the practitioner working too deeply. Let clients who are new to massage know that it is common to feel a little soreness the day after their first massage, especially if they are requesting deep pressure. After your session concludes, explain that massage may release stored tension or toxins and educate them on post-massage self-care to help limit soreness or discomfort. Encourage clients to drink plenty of water to flush the systems, eat nutrient-rich foods and take a warm bath with Epsom salts. This way, if a client wakes up a little sore the next day, they will know ahead of time that it is a natural occurrence.

Even the best of therapists will occasionally have "one of those days." There is not much you can do with an irrational client other than take a deep breath, stay calm and centered, and chalk it up to an interesting experience. In these instances it's important that you have a friend, especially another massage therapist, to share your experience with. My therapist friends were invaluable to me when I was first starting my practice, and now I try to return the favor by helping and listening to students and new practitioners whenever I can.

## SEX & MASSAGE

"Sooo… do any of your clients ever, get a, uhhh, *you know?*"

Even though times are changing, be prepared to get this question every now and again as a massage therapist. Typically it is asked by men who have had very limited experience with massage therapy. Try not to take it personally, as the question is typically rooted more in ignorance and curiosity than anything else.

"*You know*" translates to mean an erection, a completely normal biologically occurring event among the male of the species. An erection in and of itself is nothing to be concerned about; it is the few men who attempt to act on their sexual impulse who are problematic. More on this later…

In our modern Western culture, all one need do is turn on the television to know we're rather confused when it comes to touch, the human body and sexuality. Touch is a necessary, vital component in the universal expression of care. But compared to many other societies, adult Americans are less prone to touching one another or showing affection outside of our romantic relationships. If you travel to other parts of the world, you will see grown children holding hands with their siblings, men hugging one another goodbye, and sons walking with their arms around elderly parents. Touch and affection are a normal part of daily life, *throughout life*.

For many of us though, we have been socialized to be affectionate only early in a relationship (when we are courting a mate), when we have young children, or when we are having sex. Because they have never known anything different, for many men, sadly, caring touch equates with sex and is limited to their romantic partner. Therefore, it can be especially life-changing to open such individuals up to massage therapy and teach them by example that showing love and care is without limitation and comes in many forms, not just sex alone.

Human touch is a necessary and vital part to a whole, fulfilled human being. If I had my way we would all get hugged and kissed and massaged every day, but short of that, we all need meaningful and caring touch every once in awhile to thrive.

Over the years, clients will come to you for all sorts of reasons… injuries to fix, stress to release, muscular knots to untie. But many of them will also come simply to be touched with compassion and caring. During our adult years, unless we are in a romantic relationship, we can go for long periods of time without being touched – massage therapy helps fill that void, a quality of immense value in and of itself.

All that said, erections are a naturally occurring phenomenon. If you practice massage for any length of time, it is bound to occur with one of your clients every once in awhile. It typically makes the client feel mortified, and some men worry about it happening so much that they won't get a full body massage out of fear of embarrassment!

One sign that a client may have an erection and is embarrassed is if you ask them to turn over after working on their backside and they resist doing so, asking if you can "just keep working on their back." Usually it is fine to humor them and keep them face down; use your judgment. If they do turn over and you notice an erection, I suggest keeping some thick, heavy blankets - wool, for example - handy to cover the sheet with. The extra security and camouflage usually puts the client back at ease, allows them to relax again, and gives the erection time to subside.

> *If a client shows any overt signs of arousal, do not attempt to work on their stomach, hips, glutes or upper legs. Instead, you can work on their feet until the moment passes.

On the other hand, sometimes we will have to deal with a client who requests sex or mistakenly assumes that is what massage is. Here are some tips on how to prevent and handle these occasions:

### SCREENING ON THE PHONE

If you advertise your massage practice in the newspaper, Yellow Pages or other vast public directory, you will undoubtedly come across this problem much more often than if you grow your practice through word of mouth and targeted advertising outlets.

Take extra care to screen non-referred, new clients if you are female, especially if you work alone out of your home or leased office space.

Most clients calling for sex will be male (not always, but the large majority.) While you have them on the phone, some common red flags to watch out for are:

- Caller requests an immediate or same-day appointment.
- Caller asks what you look like.
- Caller wants reassurance that a woman will give him a massage.
- Caller asks what you will be wearing.
- Caller asks if he can have his massage without sheets covering him.

- Caller asks if "you will do anything else besides massage?"
- Caller gives you either a very generic or odd name that sounds phony. For example, Bob Smith or Donald Duck.
- Caller has left a voicemail requesting an appointment very late at night.

Unless you are distracted while you're on the phone, you will usually be able to intuit if someone is not legitimate. If you aren't one hundred percent sure about someone but decide to go ahead and book the session anyway, some further precautions you can take are:

- Get a first AND last name, and preferably home and work phone numbers.
- Ask how they were referred to you, and if their answer is anything other than word-of-mouth, you may wish to reaffirm that you offer professional, therapeutic massage. Inquire what type of work they are looking for.
- Book the client when an office mate is immediately next door or someone else is around nearby.
- Call both home and work numbers in order to confirm the session the day before and make sure that the client's name and number are legitimate.
- When the client arrives, be professionally dressed (nothing revealing or sloppy) and maintain a friendly but no-nonsense attitude.

In the event a client does act on a sexual impulse, it will typically not be anything sudden or shocking. Instead, they will begin doing subtle things in order to test your boundaries. These may include:

- Trying to hold your hand (while you're massaging their arm or hand)
- Touching you when you are standing along the side of the table
- Grinding and rocking their hips when they are facedown on the table
- Requesting that you work on their inner thighs or glutes excessively
- Complimenting your looks or body
- Asking if they need to be covered by a sheet (often adding that their "last therapist didn't make me use a sheet")
- Asking if they can have their massage on the bed instead of the massage table (often adding that "this is how it's done in Asia" – feel free to remind them they are not currently in Asia)

If any of these things occur, I recommend immediately stopping the session and reaffirming your massage is strictly therapeutic in nature. Then, if you feel comfortable doing so, you may give them the option of continuing or ending the session. More often than not they will deny doing anything inappropriate, cease any sexual behavior and you will be able to finish the session without incident.

Alternatively, some clients will want to talk about sex, ask you about your love life, or be overly flirtatious. Occasionally you may have a client who stares at you while you are working in a manner that makes you feel weird. While these behaviors aren't necessarily threatening, they can be annoying. To combat inappropriate talk or questions, you can always attempt to change the subject. Don't allow clients to pry into your personal life, and graciously redirect their attention to their body. A simple way to deal with a client's staring at you is to put an eye pillow over their eyes. Or, cover their face with a warm towel with a little space over their nose left open so they can breathe. This feels really relaxing and effectively covers their eyes and mouth at the same time.

Occasionally you may find yourself sexually attracted to a client. In this instance you will need to explore within yourself if you will be able to set aside your feelings and maintain firm boundaries when working with that client. If you're unsure, please do what is in the best interest of your client and discontinue working with them. It's not fair to your client to sexualize your work with them. Remember, their massage is all about them, not about you!

## Do Your Part

Society has come a long way in recent years to validate and legitimate bodywork and massage therapy. This is largely due to the hundreds of thousands of massage therapists out there doing therapeutic massage and contributing to the vast growth of the industry. Together we have all raised the public's consciousness.

However, there are still misconceptions about massage therapists floating around, with many inexperienced individuals associating massage with hippies, hookers or hefty foreign women slicking you over with oil and pummeling away. We still also have the frustration of prostitution being practiced under the name of "massage," especially in urban and Asian communities. The popular news media continues to mistakenly use the term "masseuse" in reference to those practicing prostitution, which only perpetuates existing misconceptions.

The more we make ourselves visible as legitimate therapists, conduct our practices as professionals, raise the profile of the massage therapy industry, and seize opportunities to educate or introduce therapeutic massage to the public, the better it will be for the industry as a whole. It is an exciting time to be a massage therapist as this ancient art blossoms in modern times and is increasingly recognized as a mainstream health practice. We all have a valuable role to play in shaping the future and perception of professional massage therapy.

### Firing a Client

Over the course of a long-term practice, you will undoubtedly encounter the occasion where it is in your best interest to let go of a client. When you are a new therapist, one of the vital lessons you will learn is the ability to work with a variety of individuals. But the more established you become, however, the freer you can be in crafting your ideal clientele.

In time, you may find that certain clients become more physical effort than they are worth, while others are overly emotionally draining. For example, you may have a client who requires an enormous amount of physical energy and asks for deeper work than your body can comfortably perform. This client may be so physically demanding that you cannot work on any other clients on the day you see this one. In this circumstance it is safer for your body and more cost-effective as well to let this client go, preserve your strength and be able to see multiple clients instead of just this one. Likewise, you may have a client who is so emotionally needy and draining that you feel like the life has been sucked out of you for a few days after seeing them. Again, it is not worth continuing to see this client if it impacts your well-being and ability to work with clients in the days following. You may one day be faced with a client who repeatedly tests your sexual boundaries, never doing anything overt but subtly implying and leaving you with a vague, icky feeling. Often these clients will overpay or tip you really well in an effort to incent you to keep seeing them, but no client should ever leave you feeling icky.

Remember, if you are feeling resentful inside about working with a client, you really aren't doing any favors for your client either. An interesting phenomenon occurs when you let go of clients that aren't assisting your growth or inadvertently causing you physical or mental harm. Almost always, as soon as you let them go, something or someone will fill that void in an extremely positive way. Too many therapists function in a scarcity mindset, worrying about the lost revenue or negative feelings a client may feel once you no longer work with them. Concentrate on the clients you do want, not what may happen if you lose one or two you'd rather move on from. Trust that the universe will take care of you and occasionally give it the space and opportunity to prove it.

Massage is a very personal practice, and our clients can become very attached and reliant upon us. If you need to let go of a client, be gentle and mindful that it may cause them some level of distress, or they may take it very personally. We can't please everyone all the time in life, but we can do our best to communicate honestly and with sensitivity.

## Clients with Emotional Issues & Trauma History

A surprisingly large segment of the population has been affected by childhood trauma and abuse. As a massage therapist it is necessary to have some familiarity and background when these clients appear on your table.

For childhood survivors of abuse, massage therapy can be extraordinarily beneficial to their recovery and healing. But, you should proceed delicately and mindfully. If you know someone who was abused as a child, you are already aware of the extreme toll it takes on the survivor's life and how much healing is necessary.

Victims of abuse often mentally cope with their trauma by repressing it (some may not even have memories of the abuse, or the memory may surface later in life.) Others completely leave their bodies, also known as disassociation. As you work with more and more clients, you will be able to sense when a client has "left their body." It can often be perceived as a vague sense of disembodiment, or a general disconnection between bodily sensations and feeling. Often these clients can withstand more pressure than seems necessary, or you will sense an absence or lack of energy in one or more parts of their body. They will feel "checked out."

Occasionally a client will disclose the abuse at the outset of your work together, and if so you may let them know that bodywork – in the course of healing – may trigger an emotional response and it is completely normal. Work with trauma clients to first bring them back into their body, with gentleness, patience and sensitivity. Remember, many of these clients' early experience of touch was neither loving nor pleasurable, so it may take years of steady work until they can begin to experience touch in this way.

Be sensitive to cues, verbal and nonverbal, when you might be triggering a reaction. The first time a client experiences an emotional release or flashback on your table can be an unnerving experience. A reaction can take many forms; the client may grow angry, begin sobbing or shaking, go still and 'cold,' or any variety of emotional symptoms. Take some deep breaths, stay grounded and remember you don't need to "do" anything but stay present with your client. Let the client know you're there, but don't ask probing questions or try to make sense of what is happening. Often the client herself doesn't know what is happening, and asking questions may make her feel more out of control than she already feels. Try your best to stay calm, speaking and moving very slowly and quietly until the moment passes.

Similarly, you can expect clients to experience emotional release due to present or recent life circumstances as well. Reassure your clients that they should never feel embarrassed about crying or becoming emotional during their time with you. Hold open a safe, nonjudgmental space of healing. Clients are not looking for you to "fix" their problem nor tell them what to do, but simply to provide them with space and quiet compassion. I encourage my clients who are moving through a loss or heartache to receive massage as often as they can, as it helps to process and release emotions.

After a particularly intense session, I will usually check-in with the client sometime over the next few days. Depending on the client, I may telephone them or use email just to see how they are feeling and let them know I care. Trust your intuition in these circumstances.

Occasionally you will have a client who may need treatment that goes beyond what we as massage therapists are able to provide. In these cases, it is valuable to have some trusted medical or psychological resources to refer to (ideally these resources also believe in massage therapy as a complementary healing path.) Massage therapy can be a very powerful adjunct healing modality when combined with talk and counseling therapies, but it cannot replace them. If your practice comes to include a lot of emotional release work, you may wish to form professional relationships with a few psychologists, counselors and social workers.

## A Special Note to Male Therapists

In many massage markets, male therapists may discover special challenges to establishing and building a practice. Massage therapy, today, is a female-dominated profession. In fact, according to statistics, 85% of practicing massage therapists are women. Knowing this at the outset can assist you in overcoming many obstacles and prevent you from getting frustrated early in your career.

Resorts, spas and outcall massage requests tend to slant heavily toward female therapists. Many male clients still have an issue with "a man touching them," and will only allow a woman to massage them. Alternatively, many female clients have had traumatic experiences in life where men have abused or harmed them in some manner, and they too may be most comfortable with a female therapist.

In the time I have spent booking massages for other therapists, I have definitely found that a large number of clients say they would prefer a woman at the outset. However, I could often overcome their hesitation to book with a man by stating that I had personally experienced his work and proceeded to describe it in glowing terms. The key was *trust*; since I was willing to personally recommend the therapist, the client was better able to trust them, even over the phone. The lesson in this for male therapists is to focus on projecting, building and maintaining the perception of trust in your practices. This can be more difficult to achieve in a transitory work setting such as destination spas or resorts, (where the clientele is a revolving door of new guests) but applicable to most other workplaces and private practices.

Take extra care with boundaries and proper, secure draping. Make sure your strokes don't veer too closely to vulnerable areas, and always ask new female clients if they would appreciate work on more sensitive areas before diving right in. Don't be overly huggy or touchy with clients, and never take your shirt off during a massage no matter how hot the room may be. If you tend to overheat or sweat a lot, wear a headband or second undershirt instead. Finally, please do not hit on your clients or ask them on a date while they are naked on your table; this is an extremely unfair and unprofessional position to put your client in. If you would like to ask them out, do not do so during their appointment (remember, it's their massage experience, not yours!) but instead at an alternative time.

Another topic that is worth mentioning is that some male therapists – especially when they are starting out – occasionally display some ego challenges. Part of the problem is our still-prevalent macho, tough-guy cultural stereotypes that continue to teach men that to be caring, compassionate and nurturing means that you are being "soft."

Some male therapists feel the need to compensate for this by being overly aggressive, working too deeply, or claiming expert status upon graduating from massage school. Unfortunately most cases I have heard from clients who had been injured by their therapist involved male practitioners who lacked sensitivity, didn't listen to the client's needs, or were working beyond their capabilities.

Before you get too down, there are a number of advantages male therapists have! Men's physicality and strength advantage lends itself extremely well to the deeper massage modalities such as deep tissue, Rolfing and structural forms of bodywork. Deeply muscled athletes such as body builders, football or rugby players often require the ultra-deep work that very few female therapists can physically perform. Many men are able to give more and longer sessions in a day without tiring or injuring themselves. Men usually have bigger hands and longer arms, and can therefore excel at client stretching and range of motion exercises. Finally, you can be an all-important role model for a society that desperately needs to be shown that men can be strong, vital and energetic as well as caring, compassionate and loving.

# CHAPTER 11
## GROWING YOUR CLIENT BASE

### Active Marketing

Long before you open your office doors, sit down and craft a first year marketing plan for your business. Trust me, when you get busy with clients, the last thing on your mind will be advertising for more! But it is crucial that you keep up your marketing efforts and spread them out over the course of the year. Often times, advertising and marketing will not pay off until many months after the time it is implemented. Think of your promotional efforts as sowing tiny seeds now that will become flowers next season.

Active marketing is every action you take to promote, market and advertise you and your practice. It includes networking, placing an advertisement, creating and distributing flyers and business cards, holding educational seminars, and more. You will get the most out of your active marketing efforts if you are strategic and consistent, so it is vital to write it down and schedule time for marketing just as you would for regular appointments.

### Passive Marketing

Passive marketing is you being you! This type of marketing encompasses the image you portray, how you speak about massage, and how you present yourself and your practice. Focus on presenting yourself in a way that inspires trust and confidence. Personality is very important when it comes to establishing a career in massage. If you are highly skilled and get great results, you may acquire clients despite not being the most likeable person on Earth. But because massage therapy is such a personal service, it is ideal if your clients like both your work and *you*.

Other forms of passive marketing include your website and promotional items that you and your clients can carry around in public, such as pens, tee shirts, water bottles, travel mugs, etc. These items should have your logo and contact information prominently displayed. The purpose of passive marketing is to create and leave a memorable, positive impression of you and your practice in the course of your daily life.

## Marketing Materials & Calendars

Business Cards: Yes, they matter, and yes, you need them! There are many low-cost, online companies that make very professional business cards quite inexpensively. I've seen many therapists make the mistake of carrying "business cards" that consist of paper squares they cut out and scrawled their number on with a pen. Avoid the uber-basic, generic cards; the idea is to make people want to keep and save your card, so all the better if it is memorable and unique-looking.

For less than what you'll earn in a couple massages, you can have high quality, polished business cards. Keep some with you at all times, as you never know when you'll run into an opportunity to meet your next client. I've learned to keep some business cards around everywhere… in my massage bag, purses, wallet, glove compartment, etc. Better yet, ask new acquaintances for one of their business cards and follow-up with them via mail or email. This way you don't leave the introductory contact up to them, and it gives you the ability to offer them a first-visit promotion in your initial outreach.

Before your cards go to the printer, double and triple-check for errors — have a trusted friend proofread them for you — and make certain they contain all your basic contact information. Cards should contain your name, title (CMT, LMT, Bodyworker, Massage Therapist, etc.), telephone number, email address, and website address, if applicable. Have the cards cut to the standard business card size so they can be easily placed into a wallet.

Low-Cost Flyers & Postcards: It is very easy and inexpensive to create professional one-page flyers to promote your massage therapy practice. If you are graphic-design-challenged, offer to trade a design student or professional in exchange for a massage. The vast majority of people are highly visual in nature; never underestimate the positive effect great design can have on your practice! Be sure that your print materials boldly display your contact information (your email address, website or phone number) and make it easy and straightforward for prospective clients to reach you.

Postcards can make wonderful mini-brochures that are both succinct and affordable. Plus, they are multipurpose, giving you the option of handing them out in person, posting them for new clients to pick up, or using them as promotional mailers. (Postcards are mailed at a lower rate than regular letters, saving you money on postage, too!)

You may have better marketing results if you include a clear, professional headshot photograph on your flyers. In my experience, a professional headshot is every bit as important as a logo. Massage therapy is a very personal service that requires trust on the part of the client; you should appear professional, approachable and safe enough to touch them. Having a face – rather than just a random phone number – is memorable and builds trust and familiarity.

One of the keys to marketing is consistency, so choose a few images, phrases and your logo carefully as you will be using them for a long time and in many different mediums. Ideally, your marketing message should translate well into many forms: print, web, business cards, radio or television. Long after you tire of looking at the same images or advertising, keep it going! Don't change just for the sake of changing, and remember that it takes much longer than you realize for your message to reach consumers.

Having a year-round marketing calendar in place - with scheduled activities and promotions - will provide you with structure and focus. Book your marketing activities into your planner just as you would a massage session. Then, even if things temporarily slow down, you will always have work to do to keep you busy and proactively building your practice.

## Seasonality in the Massage Industry

Depending on where you live, you will typically have busier and slower times of year that become predictable the longer you practice in your community. For example, in the San Francisco Bay Area we welcome many tourist travelers from June through September. In October we receive large numbers of conference attendees, December brings lots of gift certificate requests and on Valentine's Day many couples arrive for romantic get-away weekends. Each of these segments needs to be marketed to differently for optimal results, and each city or community will be a little different.

Some seasonal fluctuations are standard no matter where you are in the United States. For example, people tend to cut back on spending just before and after tax time in April. June also tends to be slower as children are beginning their summer vacations and everyone's schedules are changing. In July and August families are taking their yearly vacations and may be out of town for weeks at a time. The longer you practice massage, the more you will recognize patterns of demand and build them into your marketing calendar and work schedule.

For your first couple of years in business, keep track of the overall number of massages you do per week, per month and per year. You will want to track which time periods are busy, and those that are not. Over time this information will become invaluable to your marketing efforts, as well as allow you to take a nice, relaxing vacation when you know business will be slow anyway!

Take seasonality into account when creating your marketing schedule. Aim to market for a specific holiday from six to eight weeks before and right up until that holiday occurs. For example, create some beautiful, professional holiday gift certificates in early November, and begin marketing them right away. Keep them in your office, in plain view and ready to go, so clients can conveniently pick them up at the same time they have their appointment. In the week before the December holidays, I offer to gift wrap and deliver certificates for a small additional charge. At this point, many people are exhausted and at their wit's end; they really appreciate having massage certificates as a meaningful, last-minute gift option.

## Low-Cost Marketing & Free Promotions

While it certainly doesn't hurt to purchase a paid advertisement if you can afford it, it is not necessary in building a large, consistent client base. There are many marketing and promotional avenues that cost virtually nothing, and word-of-mouth marketing tops the list.

Word-of-Mouth: Hands down, the best form of marketing! Word of mouth marketing occurs when an existing client refers a new client to you. Not only does the client do the promotional work for you, the clients they refer typically do not require the same kind of screening that strangers responding to an ad do. Always take a moment to ask new clients how they heard of you. Then, if they were referred, be sure to send an email or – better yet – a handwritten thank you note to the client who did the referring.

Education, through speaking opportunities, classes, or writing booklets or articles for the public, is another excellent low-cost way to raise the profile of your practice. You can also donate massage services to raffles, auctions, charitable organizations and special events. Your name and business logo will often be included on the sponsor's list and distributed to all event attendees, providing you with an excellent promotional opportunity.

## Networking

### NETWORKING WITH OTHER BUSINESS OWNERS

Attend community business events, clubs and meetings where business owners go to network their products and services. Seek out business owners who share the same target audience. Real estate agents, personal trainers, travel agents, nutritionists, dietitians, yoga instructors and hot tub dealers are a few great examples; they all offer personal services, too. Individuals in these professions tend to know a lot of people, and the opportunity exists to do some cross-marketing and joint promotional projects. For instance, a travel agent may put an overseas package together that includes a massage gift certificate upon their return (bodywork is always welcome after a long flight!) In return, your clients may receive a discount when they use that travel agent. The possibilities are endless; be creative!

When approaching a potential marketing partner, show interest in their business and how you can help them gain clients, too. Be prepared to *offer* something before you *ask* for something, and take time to build a relationship. Make sure you use your marketing partner's products and experience their services yourself before you refer them to anyone else. You want to be certain they are reputable and you can confidently vouch for them. If your partnership will be ongoing, or requires some outlay of money from one or both of you, it is a good idea to put your objectives in writing. You should include your individual expectations, responsibilities and the length of your proposed partnership. Don't forget to discuss and set in writing what happens if one or both of you don't follow through on your end of the deal.

When cross-marketing with other businesses, don't simply exchange mailing lists and begin calling, emailing or soliciting each other's client base. For privacy reasons, you should never sell or give out your client's names or contact information. When a client comes to you for a massage, they are trusting you to keep their information exclusive to your business. You can market *on behalf of* another business, but don't simply hand your list over.

### Networking with other Massage Therapists

Cultivating relationships with other massage therapists can be fulfilling on so many levels, and especially rewarding professionally.

With the torrid growth of the massage industry, many therapists are concerned that the market will be flooded with too many practitioners and there won't be enough clients to go around, as if there is a finite number of bodies to massage. Avoid this scarcity mentality, and don't disparage other therapists out of fear or insecurity.

I live in the San Francisco Bay Area, which is an extremely competitive market when it comes to the availability of massage and spa services. Customers have *lots* of options. The upside of this reality is that the public is very conscious and aware when it comes to massage therapy and bodywork, and we therapists do not have to overcome much resistance to booking appointments. We also have many fellow therapists we can refer and trade with, learning new skills and techniques.

Instead of being resentful or worried about losing clients to another practitioner, reverse your thinking and put your energy into expanding your market. Maybe it is time for you to learn a new modality or take that hot stone class you've been meaning to check out. Opportunities for growth are everywhere.

Strive to be open, friendly and supportive of other therapists; you will add infinitely to your practice and may make some very close friends. Build your reputation with other therapists as well as clients. Then, when a therapist needs someone to cover a client session in an emergency, they will call you. When a couple requests a tandem massage and wishes to have a second therapist at the same time, their therapist will call you. When a therapist needs to let go of a client or is too booked to take a new client, they may think of you and refer them over. See what I mean? There are myriad advantages that forging relationships with other practitioners will afford you. As a bonus, having the occasional opportunity to work alongside fellow therapists can be a wonderful change of pace from our typically solitary practice.

## Public Demonstrations – Seminars & Chair Massage

Chair massage is an excellent way to market your business, especially if you are shy when simply talking about yourself in social settings.

Performing chair massage at corporate functions, fundraisers, stores, sporting events and workplaces allows you to introduce yourself – and your work – to potential clients in sample-sized, experiential bites. Volunteer your services to organizers, event planners and business owners in exchange for the ability to hand out your business cards and information. Most will be very receptive; you will typically be a big draw and exciting addition for their guests!

You can also offer table or chair massage at fairs, health clubs, and trade shows accompanied by informational talks or educational seminars that you provide. For example, you may give chair massage from 10am-11am, followed by an informative talk about massage from 11:30-12. You can arrange to speak to groups who are likely candidates for massage, such as yoga students, athletes, or fitness club members.

## Courting the Press

Everyone loves massage, and that includes the press! Search out the most popular newspapers and periodicals in your area and determine which editors cover health, lifestyle or small business sections. Editors are inundated with emails and telephone calls, so I recommend sending them something memorable in the postal mail that stands out and hopefully avoids being tossed into the trash!

>   *When addressing editors and media people, do enough research to make sure you are sending your pitch to the right person, in the right department. Once you find them, make sure you spell their name correctly.

For example, put together a little gift package, including a gift certificate in the editor's name. Make sure it is in their specific name to make it clear it is for them and not transferable to someone else. Enclose a very brief (always be concise when dealing with busy editors) note introducing yourself and welcoming them to come in for a complimentary massage. A link to your website, if you have one, is appreciated as are a couple brief quoted testimonials from your best clients.

You may also wish to offer your availability as an "expert" in the field of massage therapy for future articles. Be sure to include your contact information, preferably a direct mobile phone number and email address, and keep in mind that writers are often on deadline and require an immediate response. In light of how busy editors are, there is no need to send a lengthy biography or resume. Instead, be creative, catchy and straight to the point.

If you are opening your own office space or clinic, you may wish to hold a Grand Opening party to introduce your new business to the community. Send press releases to the local media, especially local television stations, newspapers and magazines. Be sure to invite your existing clientele and new neighboring business owners. Once you're in business, you may occasionally host open houses at your office for the public to come learn about massage therapy and view your space. Be sure to invite the media to these events, too!

## Massage 2.0 – Internet Marketing

More and more clients are using the world wide web to seek out information about massage therapy or to locate a professional practitioner in their area. It is now possible to create a very professional, visually appealing and basic website for a minimal investment. Having your own website is like having a brochure that describes you and your practice available for viewing 24/7. It also adds a marked level of professionalism to your practice. There are a number of things you will want to include on your website, and it is best to gather and script this information before the design process begins. Some of this information includes:

- Your Biography: Remember, massage therapy is a very personal service, so use this part of your site to communicate your skills, experience and credentials and establish trust and rapport. Detail the modalities you practice and describe each as if you are writing for someone utterly unfamiliar with massage therapy or any kind of bodywork. Include a professional headshot and massage-related images.
- Frequently Asked Questions: Clients new to massage will feel more at ease if they know what to expect. Reassure and educate visitors about massage by having a FAQ page.
- Testimonials: Ask a few of your favorite or most noteworthy clients if they would provide a public testimonial for you. Let them know you would like to use it for your marketing materials and make sure it is alright with them for you to use their name.
- Express Unique Qualities: Do you have unique qualifications or expert status? Perhaps you work with an Olympic athlete, or specialize in prenatal massage. Maybe you combine massage

therapy with private yoga instruction…the possibilities are
endless. Describe any aspects that set your practice apart and
make it special.

- Location & Contact Information: Make sure to have your
  contact information prominently displayed on *each* page of your
  website.

Don't include items on your website that may change, such as your
rates, office hours, or temporary office address unless it is easy for you
to update your website. Also, you may want to insert parentheses when
listing your email address (e.g. kayse (at) soulsticespa.com) to avoid
getting overwhelming amounts of spam or junk mail.

It is a great idea to include photos of your office space, treatment room
or other massage-related pictures for your website. If you prefer, there
are many terrific stock photo companies that allow you to purchase
photography and images at a very affordable price. To find some of these
companies, type the term "stock photos" into your chosen internet
search engine. After you've found a few you like, peruse their catalog of
images, especially those massage or spa-related. Once you purchase an
image you are generally free to use it in any of your marketing materials,
including your website.

You can list useful, massage-related or health websites that you would
like to let people know about, such as www.aboutmassage.com. Link
your website to other relevant businesses and their websites, and build
traffic to your site through search engine optimization. Have other
websites link to your site as well.

You may wish to create a blog where you write about massage therapy,
or offer related tips and advice to your clientele. Make yourself available
by email to answer questions and inquiries from prospective clients.
Create a Facebook page for your massage practice, and have your
clients add themselves as "fans." List your practice on internet review
sites, such as Citysearch.com or Yelp.com, and have your clients post
positive testimonials about your work. Build your identity, practice
and connections on social networking sites, especially those related to
health, wellness and massage therapy (see massageprofessionals.com.)

*If you are electronically-challenged, please don't be put off or
intimidated by these fantastic technologies! Just ask a client or
acquaintance who is more familiar with this area to help you
create a presence for your practice on the internet; it won't be

hard to find these days, and most people would love to trade a massage for something they consider a fun way to pass the time.

You can keep in touch with your clients through email marketing newsletters. Have a place on your website where clients can sign up to receive them online. When you offer public demonstrations or chair massage, have a notebook out where people may sign up to be on your list as well. I don't recommend purchasing existing mailing lists, especially random lists of email addresses. These prospects are typically cold, i.e. unscreened and have shown no predisposition toward massage therapy. Many of these addresses may not be valid, and more and more people only wish to be on the lists they personally sign up for. It may take more time for you to grow your list organically, but it will be of much higher quality once it's created.

## Targeting & Tracking

If you are at the beginning of your practice, recently relocated, establishing a new office or otherwise in a position where you need to generate clients quickly, there are a few targeted strategies you can use in these circumstances:

- Deep introductory discounts: 50% off for First-Time Clients
- Package discounts: 2 Massages for $99 (Paid for up front)
- Discount hard-to-fill or off-peak appointment times: $20 off Monday-Thursday before 2pm
- Longer sessions for the same price: A 90 minute massage for the price of a 60 minute session (An upside to this promotion is that clients usually enjoy the extra time so much that they will often stick with the ninety minute session after the promotion is over!)

Keep in mind that the above strategies are designed to get new clients in the door quickly, though possibly not long term. Always include a firm deadline with any promotions (e.g. must book by the end of the week or month) to motivate people to act immediately. With these marketing efforts, some of the individuals you draw will be the people who are always out 'looking for a deal.' You may see them once or twice, then never again. Use these types of promotions when you need to generate revenue quickly or fill some empty appointment times, not as a permanent strategy.

If you are located near a business that draws large crowds of people, it's a good idea to introduce yourself to the owner, manager and staff to offer introductory massages and perhaps an ongoing special rate if they refer clients your way. Nail salons, retail shops and nearby hotels are all great examples; these establishments see a lot of foot traffic on any given day. When I began my business we offered complimentary massages to the concierge staff at many of San Francisco's top hotels. Sometimes forming a relationship with one key person is all it takes to create a consistent stream of clients and revenue for you. Figure out who those people are to your business, court them, and once you've won them over, cherish them always!

Track your client base... Is it predominantly male, or is it mostly female? What is your client's average age? What are your most popular appointment days and times? Do you do more sixty minute or ninety minute sessions? Track your income... do you make more money on certain days than others?

Once you have this information you can use it to adjust and optimize your practice and concentrate on attracting your ideal clientele. With a bit of strategy you can get the best results while making the most of your time and marketing efforts. Take time to visualize your ideal client, and target your advertising toward the places they go, things they read and stores where they spend their money.

For example, if you love working with athletes, make it a point to advertise and network where athletes hang out, such as gyms, sporting goods stores, fitness centers and events. Take an advertisement out in a fitness-related local magazine. Offer chair massage at a bike race. Hang some flyers and introductory discount promotions where runners buy their running shoes. Get to know the physical therapists and sports medicine clinics in your area and create professional referral relationships. Immerse your marketing efforts and raise your profile in the places your clients venture most.

# CHAPTER 12

## LITTLE THINGS THAT MAKE A BIG DIFFERENCE

There are a number of common mistakes that therapists are prone to make in the early years of practice. Many of them are simply lessons you will learn through experience or by losing a client or two because of them. Hopefully, by outlining them here, you will be ahead of the game and won't need to live through them to learn from them! As you set up your office space, market your practice and build client relationships, keeping the following in mind can make a big difference to your practice...

*Feng Shui*

Set up your office space with your clients in mind. Clear any clutter and maintain a comfortable and professional environment. Cleanliness and spaciousness allow people to feel safe and relax more easily. Pick up a book or two on the principles of Feng Shui, a system that will help you place and arrange your office to maximize energy and flow. Make sure neither you nor your sheets look wrinkled or unkempt, and try to keep them matching. Avoid using crazily mismatched, threadbare or sheets with cartoon characters on them. Wash sheets and face cradles after each use; it is very unsettling for clients to find your face cradle cover streaked with someone else's mascara or foundation.

If you tend to run hot or sweat a lot, you may opt for an electric table warmer to keep the client individually toasty rather than heating the entire room. You can also dress in layers and add or remove clothing throughout your shift to accommodate fluctuating temperatures. Keep a comfortable, warm blanket available for clients who always seem to be cold (commonly women.) Make sure it is heavy, but not so heavy that it feels suffocating.

*Papa Don't Preach*

One thing I've witnessed over and over again is some therapist's tendency to lecture their clients. It is wonderful to be enthusiastic and encouraging about health and wellness, but people are not coming to us to be evangelized. By all means, share your education, experience and information – many clients will come to view you as a resource and ally in their quest for health and well-being – but make an effort not to be self-righteous or preachy about it.

If you have boarded a particular bandwagon, take care not to push your beliefs on your clients. This might be a religious group you are part of, a political cause you support or a spiritual practice you have begun. You may become a follower of a guru, a fan of a personal development course or coach, or get great results from a multi-level-marketed nutritional supplement system. As we become close with our long-time clients, it is natural you will come to share things with them regarding your personal life; just take extra care that you are sharing your personal story, not sermonizing or telling them what to do. Maintain good boundaries and appreciate that different things appeal to different people.

In the client-practitioner relationship, the client is in the more vulnerable and receptive position, literally in the hands of the therapist. Remember, the massage experience is theirs, and the session should always be about them, no matter how much you think they could benefit by following the same path or beliefs as you. If clients are made to feel like they need to buy your supplements or attend your church for you to like or care for them, then that is not fair to your client.

Smoking is bad for you. Very bad, in fact. Smokers know this, and rest assured they are reminded of it a dozen times a day. It is also well established that high heels are terrible for the feet, legs and back. But a lot of women can't imagine life without them. Remember, everyone comes to things in their own time, in their own way, and you can't force people to change their habits until they are ready to. Strive to be understanding and compassionate. Meet people at their level, speak to them in a language they can understand, and support them on their healing path, regardless of where they happen to be at the moment!

In the course of my massage work I have been amazed at the strength, depth and resilience in the human spirit. Often times the sunniest personality will surprise you with stories of their life and the extreme traumas they have overcome. Many times it is the fearful, resistant client who initially rubs you the wrong way who turns out to be a surprise and a joy to work with. Do your best to care for your clients without judgment, as you may not yet be aware of what they have been through in their lifetime. Be grateful that they have chosen to be with you at this point in their journey.

*Make Things Easy For People*

Be easily accessible by cell phone, email or text messaging. It is extremely important to return calls as soon as possible. Caller ID is priceless; make sure you have it on your office and mobile phones. When clients call to schedule a session on a certain day, sometimes they will have a time in mind. If not, give them a few *specific* times as choices rather than asking "what time is best for you?" It is much more efficient in scheduling to offer firm choices to your clients rather than leaving it open-ended. This method also gives the impression that you are a busy, in-demand therapist; not a bad thing!

Modern life dictates that people are busy and many individuals live at a rather hectic pace. There are always numerous activities and responsibilities competing for your client's time, attention and resources. Therefore, when you have them on the phone, book it! Don't leave things hanging or arrange to talk at a later time to schedule a session unless it is absolutely necessary. If it is at all possible to book the session in the moment, try your best to schedule it right away.

*Accessorize Mindfully*

Be conscious of the clothing and accessories you wear while practicing massage. In the course of a session, your client's limbs may brush against you while you're moving them around, so avoid wearing jewelry - especially rings, bracelets and watches - that might scratch them. Don't wear unwieldy or heavy belt buckles, and if you have long hair keep it pulled back so it doesn't drag over or tickle your client. Ideally your clothing should be made of soft, breathable and natural fabric that feels pleasant to the touch. Some massage moves and stretches require a client's arm or leg to rest on the therapist's person, so make sure that they are resting on a comfortable fabric, not your bare skin.

*Minimize Electronics*

Try to keep the blips and beeps to a minimum for your clients. Keep your cell phone, computer and messaging devices quieted or turned off at all times during their time with you. Believe it or not, I have witnessed massage therapists answering their mobile phone, chomping on a sandwich, listening to voicemails and replying to text messages *in the middle* of a massage session. Unless your wife has gone into labor or there is an absolute emergency, please avoid these behaviors! Give your client your undivided attention at all times.

*Be an Information Resource*

When you find an outstanding chiropractor, makeup artist, hair stylist or any other service provider, keep their information on file. Over time, your clients will get used to coming to you for all kinds of information and referrals, especially when it comes to health, wellness, and beauty. It's a great way of keeping in touch with your clients, and the other practitioners will hopefully return the favor and refer their customers over to you as well. Just make sure you only refer to professionals that you have used yourself and that you trust do great work.

*Hygiene Counts*

Make sure you have fresh breath before you begin each session, especially if you just ate smelly foods or drank coffee. Ideally, you want to avoid breathing on your client at all! When working on the neck and face from behind the client, turn your head to the side when it's time to exhale. Feeling hot breath on your face is not particularly pleasant, even if that breath smells just fine.

Don't over-perfume yourself or your massage room. Scents are powerfully connected to and influential upon our healing, hence the efficacy of aromatherapy. It is ideal to start out with a neutral, unscented environment; each client will be unique as to which scents appeal to them.

Observe your feet. Now, would you mind having to look at those feet for thirty minutes straight? That's what your clients do, so please take note! Pay attention to the shoes you wear to perform massage, or if you're like me and practice barefoot, make sure your feet and toenails won't scare people.

Keep your fingernails trimmed and cuticles softened to avoid scratching the skin of your clients.

If you smoke cigarettes, even occasionally, make sure the clothing you wear to do massage is kept completely separate from any environment in which there is cigarette smoke. Avoid smoking for the duration of your work day. Trust me, you may not smell the residue on your clothes, but your clients certainly will!

*Underpromise and Overdeliver*

By this I mean practice amazing customer service with each and every client. Always strive to be on time, and if you say you will do something, make sure to follow through. Exceed expectations whenever possible, and take care not to make promises or guarantees you can't keep. Don't short clients on time – if someone books an hour, trust that they will notice if you only do fifty minutes. Practice open, warm and direct communication with your clients, and make them feel welcome to communicate equally with you.

Don't take it personally if you learn that a client is also seeing other massage therapists or bodyworkers. It is impossible to be everything to everyone! Things change over time – muscles, moods, activities, and emotional states – and each therapist has different strengths and aptitudes. The more you practice stellar customer service and open communication, the better you will be able to adapt and continue working with a client over the course of many years.

*Be a Free Spirit... To An Extent*

One of the beauties of being a massage therapist is the mobility and freedom we are afforded in the course of an independent practice. This, in part, is what draws so many free spirits and curious seekers to the field. Once you are established in your career, you will have a lot of independence when it comes to scheduling and shaping your practice to best suit your lifestyle. But, until that day arrives, be disciplined and mindful when it comes to building your business.

Over the years I have seen many brilliant therapists damage or diminish their potential by leaving their clients in the lurch one time too many. If you are constantly breaking appointments or taking off on jaunts, your clients will ultimately view you as too unpredictable or unreliable to take care of them on a consistent basis. You can absolutely enjoy the freedom a career in massage can provide, just be careful in the early years and be strategic about scheduling. Put being there and being available for your clients among your top priorities, especially when first launching a private practice.

# CHAPTER 13

## SPECIAL CASES

### Working With Clients New to Massage

It is great fun working with clients who are brand new to massage, but there are a few things you should keep in mind to help things go as smoothly as possible. When booking a new client, and for their first few sessions, you may want to leave room in your schedule a little before and after their scheduled time. This gives you some extra time to chat and have them fill out an intake form. It also provides a cushion in the event they run late or have trouble finding your office the first few visits. Lastly, it allows you the flexibility to extend their session if they so choose.

Many clients will initially schedule a one hour massage when they're seeing a new massage therapist for the first time. The price of a massage is a significant investment for many people, and often they will want to make sure they like your work before they commit to a longer session. New clients will often opt to extend their session once they're on the table, so remember to leave room in your schedule just in case!

Be flexible when new clients request a specific type of massage. Sometimes people ask for something when they really don't know what it is. Perhaps their friend mentioned they should get a particular kind of massage, or it's the only kind they have heard of. Alternatively, they might be embarrassed to admit they have never had a massage. Don't feel the need to correct people or make them wrong, but instead gently clarify what it is they are asking for to ascertain what they really want and need.

Take special care to honor people's modesty, especially if they are new to massage. As a bodyworker, you will very quickly become comfortable around the human body and nudity. But always keep in mind that most people do not have the same level of exposure or familiarity, and very few people are entirely at ease with their body image. Take extra care when draping new clients with sheets and blankets, anchoring the edges of the sheets to help them feel secure. (By anchoring, I mean pressing the edges of the sheet down against them and tucking it under their arm or leg securely.) In time and with practice, you will be able to sense when a client is especially modest and take extra care to put them at ease.

Develop a routine for explaining to new clients how to get on the massage table. My instructions go something like this:

"Now, I am going to leave the room and give you some privacy while you get on the massage table. Please remove all your jewelry, and take off as much clothing as you feel comfortable. You will be kept under the sheets and blankets at all times, and we'll only be uncovering you as we work on different parts of your body. Most people remove all their clothing, but if you would like to keep your undergarments on, that is perfectly fine. Please start out face down under the top sheet (at this point I usually pull back the top sheet and point to the table, demonstrating what I mean), resting with your head here in the face cradle. I'll give you a few moments, and then knock before coming back into the room…"

You may wish to accompany your instructions with arm motions or visual cues, too, to help demonstrate what you are saying. Many individuals "see" more clearly than they "hear," especially when they are nervous or in a new environment. Be especially gentle and patient in your tone with new clients, who may feel silly or self-conscious. Having a consistent opening ritual will allow subsequent visits to feel routine, familiar and better allow your client to relax instantly and easily.

New clients often need a little reassurance and more instruction than usual when booking their first massage over the telephone. Avoid using lots of massage jargon, and don't be afraid to give very simple instructions and descriptions. Many people have no idea what to expect. Once I walked into the treatment room and found my client lying on top of the sheets, totally nude, except for her socks and tennis shoes. She heard me ask her to get undressed, but no instructions to remove her shoes. Lesson: What is old hat to you is a whole new world to someone else! If a new client sounds nervous or unsure on the phone, occasionally I will send them a brochure about massage (detailing what to expect and little tips) and their intake form ahead of time. This mailing serves multiple purposes:

- Re-establishes that the massage is professional and therapeutic
- Further helps put the client at ease by providing them with information
- Reminds the client of their upcoming appointment

- Gives reassuring suggestions such as where to park, what to eat before a session and what to wear
- Provides them with something they can pass on to friends or family they wish to refer to you

During your session, take care to maintain flow and contact. It is reassuring for new clients to know where you are in the room at all times. If you need to break contact for any reason, that is typically a good moment to check in verbally and inquire how they are feeling, ask if the temperature or pressure is alright, etc. They will hear your voice and know you are still beside them.

It is especially important to set expectations and educate clients who are new to massage. Occasionally clients will arrive thinking that you will fix their shoulder injury, incurred in high school thirty years ago, in just one session. New clients require equal parts application and education, and some are much more informed than others. One neurosurgeon client was able to educate me on the finer workings and nuances of the spine, while another asked me if we humans had any bones in our necks. Be ready for any extreme!

## Working with VIPs and Celebrities

*The Rich… they're not like you and me.* Or so the saying goes… In many ways, that saying is not too far off!

A high profile or celebrity client's biggest concern is typically shielding their privacy. Generally speaking, the bigger the name, the bigger the pack of photographers and paparazzi there are stalking their every move. If you have occasion to work with a famous or celebrity client, please keep the following tips in mind:

- Celebrities will often check into hotels under a false name. If someone books a session for Horton Hippo or Zelda Fitzgerald, just go with it and don't ask too many questions. You'll find out who they really are soon enough!

- Celebs often have a horde of assistants, handlers and staffers whirling around them, sometimes helping and sometimes just creating more chaos. I have found that, more often than not, the actual celebrity is like the eye of a hurricane. In other words, they are the calm in the middle of the storm. (There will be some exceptions!) Celebrities rely on the people around them to protect them, take care of their needs, and most importantly, keep the outsiders out! So, if an assistant seems unnecessarily pushy or high strung, try to be patient and don't take it personally; it's just part of their job and goes with the territory.

■ Famous clients will expect you to guard their privacy. If they confide in you, it is because they trust you, and like all clients they deserve and expect confidentiality. Most will expect you to come directly to their home or hotel room, again to protect their privacy. If you do have an office or spa they will visit, it is thoughtful to offer them a side or back door to use so they may avoid cameras or autograph seekers.

■ Don't ask them for an autograph. Occasionally they may offer anything from autographs to concert tickets to backstage passes – in these cases, feel free to take them up on it! But be sure to *leave it up to them* to offer. Remember, celebrities and famous people are often surrounded by various hangers-on, false friends and a variety of people who want a piece of their fame or money. Under all the hype, most celebs are real people under a lot of pressure, and they appreciate genuine care, respect and a safe space to relax as much as anyone.

■ If you are working with members of a royal family or foreign dignitaries, they may be much more formal than most Americans you will encounter. This formality may be due to their culture, or their station in life, but in either case try to carry yourself with the same level of service and formality they are accustomed to. For example, you may be expected to use the term "Your Highness," "Sir," "Madam" or another formal word you could never otherwise imagine yourself using! It is usually best if you limit conversation to the minimum necessary, and generally speak only when asked a direct question. Customize your manner and tone according to the client.

While it sounds glamorous to work with celebrities and high-profile clients, know that they require a great deal of flexibility and patience at times. You will need to become adaptable in terms of hours, schedules and occasionally, lifestyles. It is not unusual to wind up working very late at night or early in the morning, especially if you are on the road traveling with clients for a show or tour. While you will often get to stay in amazing resorts and hotels, make sure there is a meal and incidental budget built into your employment contract. Sometimes your only option for meals will be to eat at the resort or through room service, and the food at these locations can be extremely expensive. Make sure it is clear that these expenses will be covered by your client, lest you spend your hard earned money on fifty dollar breakfasts!

## Obese Clients

Across America, obesity and excessive body weight is at epidemic proportions, and it is inescapable that you will at some point work with an overweight client. One thing to keep in mind at all times is that—for most overweight people—it is rarely about the food. Most obese individuals, especially women, overeat to cover up what is usually an emotional or mental issue, eating to numb or hide themselves from others.

Many people who were abused as children later turn to food for comfort and grow fat in an unconscious effort to become unattractive to others. Deep down, they may see themselves as shameful, ugly, guilty or unworthy, and this may be reflected in their appearance and lack of care for themselves. Most overweight people know they are overweight, and may be very self-conscious and hesitant to be seen without their clothes on. Encourage these clients to receive massage, as learning to love and care for their body is exactly what they need most.

Many times I have heard people say, "Oooh, gross. How can you be a massage therapist? Doesn't that mean you have to touch all kinds of *fat people?*" As a society, we are very judgmental of overweight individuals, and our lack of understanding manifests in insensitive comments like this. However, with the understanding that obesity is often a sign of emotional hurt or pain, you can bring more compassion, caring and patience to your work with these clients. Bodywork can play an integral role in helping them to get healthy, heal, and feel comfortable inside their body.

## Disabled Clients

With advances in technology and medicine, many disabled individuals are able to lead dynamic, abundant and full lives. Massage therapy can be wonderful for clients with physical challenges and handicaps, as in many cases part of the body is doing more work to compensate in these individuals. For example, a client in a wheelchair may primarily use their arms for locomotion, putting an immense amount of wear on the shoulders and arms. Massage and bodywork can bring balance, release tension, and prevent injury in these vital areas.

Some conditions require that people undergo regular surgeries or procedures in the course of living with their disability. On these occasions, massage therapy can help clients prepare, recover and lower stress. In some cases, regular bodywork can lessen the effect of the disability, increase range of motion and improve the life and well-being of these clients.

If you welcome disabled and handicapped individuals into your practice, you will quickly learn that these souls are truly gifts in the world. Personally, I have been amazed and inspired by my handicapped clients. One is a championship athlete today despite missing a limb, while another is a professional dancer despite being paralyzed from the waist down. They carry themselves with so much joy and grace in their daily lives, even though they have many more challenges than the rest of us have. It is an honor to know and work with these clients.

## Children as Clients

With each subsequent generation, children are exposed to much more in life at an earlier age. Thanks to the proliferation of media, technology and access, children are more savvy and sophisticated than ever before. Therefore, many children, especially in urban and affluent areas, are exposed to spa treatments and massage therapy when their parents receive these services. For several reasons, many spas and resorts have policies that set a minimum age requirement (often age 18) for its guests. One, spas need to preserve a quiet and calm environment for their guests and two, unsupervised children may be a liability issue in a spa setting, many of which have pools and hot tubs. Many day spas and massage clinics will allow children to receive services, but only if they are a minimum age and in the company of a parent or guardian.

If you are working as an employee or independent contractor for a larger organization, the owner or management will often set and enforce any age requirement policies. However, if you are in private practice it will be up to you to decide whether or not you will work with children.

For many therapists, the first occasion to work with children (aside from their own!) is on an outcall basis. While you are providing massage for parents in the home, children will often be curious and find any opportunity to poke their head in and smile at you inquisitively while you're treating mom or dad. Eventually the child or their parent may ask for you to give them a mini-session, or they may request a full session. Personally, I love working with children and welcome them to jump up on the table for any length of time. My policy has been to work with children of all ages, but those under sixteen must have their parent around and usually in the room. It is a wise idea to have parents sign a waiver or include permission on the intake form, especially if you anticipate accepting children into your practice on a regular basis.

## Elderly Clients

Many cultures around the world revere and admire old age and take care of its elder generations. Ours? Not so much! On the contrary, our Western society fights old age with everything we've got, encouraging staying youthful in the way we look, dress and act for as long as humanly possible.

The elderly need the benefits of touch therapy and massage perhaps more than any other demographic. Regular treatment can help relieve the physical aches and pains associated with aging, maintain range of motion in the joints and flexibility, boost immunity and improve circulation. Many elderly individuals live alone for some time after outliving their spouses; these clients especially need the loving touch and community your time together can provide. When you work with older clients, you may wind up spending a lot more time engaged in conversation than you do with other customers. Depending on their health, you may be limited to very gentle massage modalities and energy work, and may need to travel to them in their home or care facility.

In working with elderly clients it is imperative that you gain some familiarity with prescription drugs and conditions related to aging. Many of these clients will have some form of arthritis; heart conditions are also very common. The elderly are often on a battery of prescription drugs for this or that, and you need to check with their physician to understand how massage may interact with their medication regimen. The extra effort is well worth it to work with these clients; they will be among your most enthusiastic, interesting and appreciative clients.

## Ill Clients

Massage therapy can make an enormously positive difference in the lives of ill and recovering clients. Because it can boost immunity, lower stress and raise endorphins, bodywork is a wonderful adjunct to the healing process. Working with ill clients can be immensely meaningful and fulfilling, but often requires specialized training so you can be certain you are helping rather than aggravating their condition.

For example, massage is contraindicated for some forms of cancer, and you should always work in conjunction with any other health practitioners involved in the client's treatment. (You will find more on general massage contraindications in Chapter 15.) It is perfectly alright if you are limited to energy work therapies for many types of cancer-related and other illnesses. Remember that your caring, compassionate presence alone can be a valuable support and boost to the mental and emotional state of a sick client.

If you come to work with a great deal of terminally ill clients or specialize in working with cancer patients, make sure you maintain a solid support system and take care of yourself emotionally. Like all therapists, you will no doubt form deep connections and bonds with your clients, and it can be extremely difficult to see them in pain or suffering or when they eventually pass on. Be sure you receive the continuous love, support and strength you need in your own life in order to do this highly rewarding and fulfilling work.

# CHAPTER 14

## CATCHING CUES & LESSONS FROM THE TRENCHES

The more experienced you become in your massage career, the more quickly you will become attuned to and intuit the needs of your clients. Many people, especially when they are new to massage, won't speak up if they are uncomfortable because they don't want to complain or come across as demanding. It will be up to you to develop your intuition as well as notice the many unspoken things that occur within a massage session. There are numerous nonverbal clues and cues you can look for and then adjust your methods accordingly. Some typical examples follow...

**SYMPTOM:**
Client is tightening up and begins flexing one of their feet.
**POSSIBLE CAUSE:**
They may be experiencing the onset of a cramp in their leg, usually the calf.
**REMEDY:**
You may wish to do some gentle stretching to ease the cramp, and make sure they have proper bolsters and support under the knees or ankles.

**SYMPTOM:**
Client is wound like a top and talking their head off.
**POSSIBLE CAUSE:**
They just need to relax and unwind before they will be able to relax into a massage.
**REMEDY:**
When clients arrive in this state, I like to begin with some deep breathing, grounding, and energy work such as Reiki. I'll also typically work on their head and scalp a little bit at the outset to release some mental energy.

**SYMPTOM:**
Client is clenching hands or feet for a moment.
**POSSIBLE CAUSE:**
The pressure was too deep, you hit a knot or painful spot, or your stroke ran too close to the spine.
**REMEDY:**
Lighten your pressure.

**SYMPTOM:**
Client is wincing.
**POSSIBLE CAUSE:**
Pressure may be too deep, or they may not like the music that is playing.
**REMEDY:**
Check in and find out.

**SYMPTOM:**
Client has goose bumps.
**POSSIBLE CAUSE:**
Client needs the temperature raised or an extra blanket.
**REMEDY:**
This is a very common occurrence in female clients, especially when clients turn face up halfway through a massage. I will often add a blanket over the sheets immediately before turning the client over if I anticipate they might otherwise become cold.

**SYMPTOM:**
Client is holding and not "giving up" their arm, leg, or neck to you.
**POSSIBLE CAUSE:**
Client may just need more relaxation. It may also be a sign that they started thinking about something and their brain is off and running.
**REMEDY:**
Gently rock the joint and bring the client back into their body. Pulse gently until you feel a release, and then do some gentle stretching. Sometimes I will also give the client a visual instruction, such as "let your leg drop like a lead weight," or "allow your arm to go loose and limp like a noodle."

**SYMPTOM:**
You are talking and your client is giving you short, one-word answers.
**POSSIBLE CAUSE:**
Client would like you to be quiet!
**REMEDY:**
This is a sign that your client would prefer to have their massage in

silence and they are being polite in not directly asking you to stop talking.

## Lessons From the Trenches

*Zip Your Lips & Throw Away the Key*

Never, ever gossip about your clients among other therapists or in public. When they are on your table, clients are trusting you with their bodies, but they are also trusting that you will protect their privacy.

The work we do is very intimate, and clients can become very open in talking about their personal lives, their hopes, dreams, fears and dramas. They deserve the courtesy of not having it all spread as gossip throughout the spa after they leave! Often you will be working with couples, families or friends and each of them may confide in you individually. It is imperative that you maintain confidentiality for each of them, particularly among one another, lest you set off a family feud. (Exceptions would be if an individual is in imminent danger or there is evidence of abuse.)

If clients ask about another client you see – perhaps their spouse or friend – it is perfectly acceptable to tactfully let them know that you honor the confidentiality of all clients. Most people have no trouble understanding this, and in fact many appreciate it when they realize you will honor their privacy in the same manner.

*Candles are Just Candles Until they Start a Fire*

I love candles. We all love candles. But I have learned the hard way why many spas and businesses don't allow open flames due to the fire danger. What did it take to convince me?

Visualize one screaming client, running from a treatment room out into the parking lot, wrapped only in a sheet with the backdrop of flames. This episode convinced me that candle bans are in fact necessary. For all those who happened to be in the parking lot that day, it appeared to be the ultimate toga party gone bad. (And yes, everyone was fine and unhurt, if slightly embarrassed.) If you enjoy the ambiance that candle light provides you may wish to try alternatives such as Himalayan salt lamps, battery operated "candles" or dimmer light switches.

*Check Your Ego at the Door*

There is never any reason to pretend to be an expert when you are not. Sure, this is true in any profession, but it holds special significance in a career that requires trust and vulnerability on the part of a client. If a client is requesting care that is beyond the scope of your education or capability, don't hesitate to refer them out to a different type of practitioner. Be confident in yourself and don't take these occasions personally or as a knock on your abilities. Different strokes for different folks!

Never assume you know better than a client. Even if they seem to be requesting something strange or unreasonable, trust their judgment and listen to what they are saying. For example, a client may request that you not work on their abdomen. Now, you may believe they *need* abdominal work and you may *want* to perform abdominal work but please, listen to what they are telling you. They may have experienced abuse and have issues being touched in this highly charged, very sensitive part of the body. Or, they may have just eaten a Big Mac and fries. Since you really don't know, take a client at their word and adhere to their requests. Strive to listen intently to your clients with your eyes, ears *and* intuition.

Ask new clients if it is alright before performing aggressive stretches or range of motion maneuvers. Some clients love these moves, while others prefer to remain entirely passive and motionless. For example, a harried client requesting a relaxation massage for stress reduction is not likely to appreciate a lot of interactive muscle testing and its associated verbal instructions. Remember, massage therapy is all about the client.

On the other end of the spectrum, don't apologize or minimize being a massage therapist. I've come across a number of practitioners who carry around an inferiority complex disguised as a massive chip on their shoulders about "just being a masseur." Often they will introduce themselves by saying they "do massage, but just for the time being until I get my big break in acting" or "I'm only doing massage until I get into physical therapy school." These types of statements do a disservice to both you and your fellow massage therapists and diminish massage as a valuable health care practice. Plus, they plant seeds of incompetence in the mind of your client, making people feel as if you're above and unconcerned about their massage experience. The more you truly believe yourself to be a professional and carry yourself as such, trust that people will give you the admiration and respect of a professional.

*Sticky Fingers… and I Don't Mean the Oil You're Using*

People will steal anything that is not bolted down. Seriously. I have never had an issue with my clients, of course, but if you share a space or common areas, please protect anything of value to you. When I shared an office space with other practitioners and their clients, I had everything from toilet paper to tissues to hundreds of dollars worth of essential oils stolen. It's not necessary to chain things to the floor or put unsightly locks on everything; just use your judgment and keep valuables safe.

Speaking of sticky, if you travel with your massage table and supplies, you may want to keep your oils and lotions inside a zippered, watertight plastic bag in case there is a spill or leak. When you buy a new bottle of oil or lotion, check that the lid has been closed all the way as soon as you purchase it. Wrap glass bottles inside bubble-wrap and keep them upright in a pocket of your massage table cover or car.

*Give Clients Their Personal Space*

This may sound slightly counterintuitive, being that your business is touching people, but when greeting clients and while they are still getting to know you, give clients enough personal space. Avoid being overly 'huggy' with brand new clients. Likewise, don't start massaging people in public or rubbing the shoulders of acquaintances without permission. Put a group of massage therapists in any given room and you're near guaranteed to have a Kumbaya moment on your hands. We are, generally speaking, a warm, affectionate and touchy-feely bunch… but remember, not all people are, especially around someone they don't yet know well.

Americans, in particular, tend to be very protective of their personal space. Over time, as clients become more familiar with you, you may feel freer in giving them a hug in greeting or goodbye. Many folks would welcome a friendly neck rub now and again, just be sure to ask first. Male massage therapists should take extra care in giving their female clients plenty of personal space and avoid making your client uncomfortable by being unexpectedly or overly affectionate.

*Express Yourself Through Your Work, Not Your Appearance*

It is a well-known fact of human nature that we gravitate toward and feel most comfortable around people who look and act like us. Knowing this, you may be self-limiting your practice if you dress or appear in a way that alienates groups of people. In time, as you establish a large practice and following, you will be able to look however you please. But while you're relatively new and inexperienced you want to be as approachable and accessible to the greatest amount of people possible. Plus, you don't want clients to miss out on your work just because they can't get past what you look like or how you dress.

I know a number of immensely talented massage therapists who unnecessarily limit their practices because they insist on dressing in colorful robes, wearing small tusks between their nostrils or having dreadlocks that could house a bird's nest. Yes, they have every right to personal expression, but they are also always short on clients – and their rent.

As a field, massage therapy tends to draw many curious, free-thinking types of people who thrive on independence, growth and spiritual seeking. Entering the world of massage and healing work can be a catalyst for tremendous personal growth and change, and occasionally individuals desire a new look or name that they feel better represents their evolving identity. If it is very important for you to change your look or name, think through how this might impact people's impression of you and your ability to draw new clients from the mainstream public.

When you're first starting out, strive to be the kind of therapist that someone could comfortably send their grandmother to. You want to appear trustworthy, safe, competent and organized. Be as free-spirited and unique as you want to be in your private life, but for the sake of your practice aim to have a broad appeal, especially when you are new to massage. Otherwise you may limit your client base to people who are just like you. Remember, it is often the people who appear most different from us that we stand to learn the most from. People can surprise you when you least expect it; give them the chance!

*Things to Keep On Hand in Your Work Area*

It is a good idea to keep oil, lotion and possibly a cream on hand in case your client has a preference. After you practice massage therapy for some time, you will no doubt find your favorite oil, lotion or specific brand. However, from time to time you may have a client who requests that you not use oil, for example. If you have an alternative on hand you can easily accommodate this kind of request.

Keep at least one fragrance-free oil or lotion available in case your client requests it. Occasionally clients will be going straight back to work or out to a dinner and may not want to smell flowery or like they just had a massage. Try to accommodate them, especially if you don't have a shower facility for them to use.

Carry a receipt book for those clients who request one. I like to keep a spare receipt book in my massage table bag; it's small and lightweight, and that way I know I always have it handy. Clients may request a receipt for their personal use or to submit to their insurance. You can easily find all-purpose receipt books for just a few dollars at most office supply stores.

Maintain a variety of music for your clients. Many therapists choose to use their iPod, a very travel-friendly way to go if you do a lot of on-site massage work. Another option is subscribing to a satellite or cable music station that provides you with all-day, commercial-free music appropriate for massage. For example, many will have a classical or new age station you can tune to. This is an excellent option if you share office space with other practitioners; everyone has different taste in music and this route standardizes the music for everyone. Plus you can all pitch in to cover the cost.

Store extra blankets in your office space. Heavy blankets can be expensive and laborious to clean, but by keeping the blanket on top of the sheets and away from oils and lotions, you will minimize the number of times you need to have it cleaned.

*Is it Real, or is it Fake?*

Occasionally you may be presented with a client who has had plastic surgery or otherwise added physical enhancements to their person. Common ones are breast implants, chest (pectoral) implants, hairpieces, hair extensions and wigs. Some individuals will tell you about their procedure straightaway, or it may be relatively obvious. In these instances it is usually easy to make some minor adjustments with bolsters and pillows or simply avoid certain parts of the body. For example, it can be uncomfortable for clients who have had dramatic breast augmentation to lie face down for an extended period of time unless some extra padding or pillow is provided.

If you practice massage therapy over the course of many years you will undoubtedly come across more than you ever knew was possible in the realm of surgical enhancement. Usually it presents no problem or contraindication for massage, but rather some minor precautions. Do your best to make your client feel comfortable without making a big deal out of it. Take care not to pull or yank on a client's hair if it is obvious they have a wig, extensions or hairpiece on. You will also want to avoid getting lotion or oil in these clients' hair since they can't wash it away with a quick shower and shampoo. When it comes to wigs, weaves and complex hairstyles it may be best to just not go there; always ask the client!

It can be a little trickier if clients have clearly had surgery but they deny having done so. I once tried to provide deep tissue for a woman who complained of sciatic pain and had extraordinarily tight glutes. As I chiseled away to no avail, I repeatedly asked the client what had created such tension. I had never felt anything like it. She replied that she "was very into hiking" and that was probably the cause. It wasn't until working her hamstrings later in the session that I made out the outline of the implants. Only then did she admit undergoing plastic surgery several years prior to have glute implants inserted. Her butt was as dense as heavy plastic because her butt *was* heavy plastic!

If a client fails to disclose any of the above, there are a few common signs that can help you determine if something is "real or fake." One, implants are not impacted by gravity the way real human tissue is, and will tend to stick straight up in the air or have an unnatural buoyancy to them. When your client is lying on their back, normal breast tissue will fall to one side or the other, whereas implants will remain straight up. Human hair comes in many textures and types, but hairpieces — no matter how well done they are — tend to have the consistency of animal fur. Massaging a toupee kind of feels like petting a squirrel (not that I assume you have pet many squirrels.)

The bottom line is that if something feels a bit off or not quite human, it probably isn't. The key is to work mindfully, tread lightly and slowly if something feels strange and make adjustments with sensitivity.

# CHAPTER 15

## MASSAGE CONTRAINDICATIONS & UNIVERSALLY ANNOYING THINGS TO AVOID

Contraindications are conditions when massage is not recommended without the approval or supervision of a physician and may include:

- Fever
- Inflammation (don't work directly on the inflamed area unless you are practicing very gentle energy work, Reiki, polarity, etc.)
- Flu
- Infections
- Contagious illnesses
- Hernias
- Heart conditions
- Cancer
- Skin rashes
- Osteoporosis
- HIV/AIDS

Note: In some areas it's not legal to ask someone to disclose if they have HIV or other illnesses, but on some occasions (if you volunteer to work with HIV patients, for instance) you may know in advance.

Some of these conditions may respond to gentle forms of energy work, but always avoid deep tissue or aggressive modalities if your client discloses or displays symptoms of any of the above conditions until you receive the written approval of their doctor.

Performing massage therapy should also be avoided if a client is obviously intoxicated and under the influence of drugs or alcohol.

On the other hand, there are a number of actions that can best be categorized as Universally Annoying Things To Avoid, as widely reported by clients. Take note! When you are giving a massage, you should generally avoid the following actions unless your client specifically requests it...

- Don't poke clients in the eye and/or work on their eyelids, even with a light touch.

- Try not to sigh heavily as if you are bored, distracted or would rather be anywhere else in the world. Moaning should also be avoided, especially the kind that sounds like you are in rapture or possessed.

- Avoid shaking naked, exposed people. Rocking modalities that require gentle shaking (e.g. Trager work) are wonderful, but please respect people's modesty. As you rock them, it is best to keep them covered by the sheet so any "jiggling" skin won't be exposed. This is especially true for women while working the hip, glute and thigh areas.

- Don't stick your fingers inside and "plug" the client's ears.

- Unless you are also a licensed and practicing chiropractor or osteopath, never attempt to adjust a client's spine. No matter how much a client begs you to "crack their back," just say no!

- If you tend to sweat a lot, keep a hand towel nearby or wear a headband. Dripping sweat on your client is icky.

- Avoid working on a client's exposed stomach and abdominal area without permission. This part of the body is extremely "charged" and can be very vulnerable in some clients. Therefore, while a lot of very powerful healing work can be accomplished by working this area, it is best to get permission from your client first and then proceed very slowly and mindfully.

- Take care not to work on your client's structure as if they are a car, boat or flooring. Remember, there is much more to a human being than their bones, skin and musculature. When you touch someone, you are touching *all* parts of them, including their spirit and soul…Even if you have a "fix it" mentality, always strive to develop your sensitivity and intuition.

- Drape your client consciously and with care, but don't go overboard. There is no need to mummify your living client. Similarly, avoid creating a giant diaper with the sheets, or tucking the sheets in between a client's buttocks. These things are unnecessary and feel really weird for the client. If you incorporate a lot of stretching and range of motion work, you may want to let your client know ahead of time so they may keep their underwear or loose shorts on if they are at risk of feeling exposed.

- Avoid prying into your client's personal life. Unless your client volunteers personal information to you, please don't inquire as to their marital status, divorce proceedings, or other personal information. Likewise, never ever ask your client on a date while they're on the table. This is never a good idea.

- Don't stretch people too aggressively. A thoughtful gesture is to ask clients before proceeding if they would like to be stretched out. This gives them a heads up that you will begin and the chance to provide verbal feedback. Some clients dislike stretching, so this gives them the opening to say so. Go slowly and avoid any sudden twisting or pulling on the joints or neck. Gently position and move the client, transitioning with grace and connectivity.

- Avoid using hot rocks in strange ways. I've had clients report hot stone massage sessions that resulted in burn marks or other various weird sensations. One client had a therapist place heavy rocks on top of an eye pillow, resulting in the client feeling like their eyeballs were being pressurized (not very pleasant.) Another was left alone for fifteen minutes with pebbles placed precariously between each toe while they strained to keep them in place (ditto!)

- Avoid getting essential oils in the eyes of your client. If you soak or infuse hot towels with essential oils take special care that you don't cover the client's face with them. Many oils will irritate or sting the eyes and mucus membranes.

There are a number of particularly sensitive places on the body that are best avoided unless a client requests it or you're working on a specific issue. These include:

- The throat
- The ear notch at the jaw bone, behind and under the ear
- Armpit
- Abdomen

- Kidneys
- Popliteal area (back of the knee)
- Groin

Take care to avoid diagnosing medical conditions. If you feel a lump in your client's body, please do not stop the session and suddenly exclaim that you've found a tumor. All this will do is understandably freak your client out. If you see or feel something unusual, inquire with sensitivity and describe how it looks or feels. Typically your client is already aware of it and can tell you exactly what it is.

Symptoms that would fall under this category are skin rashes, bruises, lumps, bumps, adhesions, sores and inflammations. Take care not to work on these specific areas or apply any direct pressure until you know for certain what it is.

> *Very common in human beings are lumpy, irregular masses of adipose tissue that feel like small-to-medium sized bumps under the skin. I've found them in both men (usually in the torso, back or midsection) and women (often in the thighs and right under the buttocks), and they are usually just harmless pockets of fat tissue. You may gently ask to see if your client is aware of it, but take care not to alarm them. Chances are it is harmless.

Every once in awhile you will have a client arrive and announce they're getting a massage because they are sick and don't feel well. While massage is contraindicated for severe illnesses, often clients won't let you know they are sick until they're already on your table, coughing, sneezing or wheezing. After a session with a sick client, thoroughly disinfect your hands, the face rest and the doorknobs in your office. You may also wish to diffuse an antibacterial essential oil into the air such as lavender, citrus or eucalyptus. These actions will help protect you and your other clients in the event what they have it contagious.

Protect yourself, too, and take extra care to wash your hands thoroughly and avoid touching your face. If you practice outcall massage, you may wish to keep a portable, antibacterial hand gel in your massage bag and vehicle. During cold and flu season, boost your immune system by eating a nutritious, vitamin-rich diet, exercising, and getting plenty of sleep. Unlike many desk jobs, the physical demands and close personal contact massage requires necessitates that we operate at a high level of health and performance. By keeping up your strength and resistance, your body will be able to fight off the germs and bugs that will occasionally show up along with your clients.

# CHAPTER 16

## BUSINESS BASICS FOR MASSAGE THERAPY

Yes, I know… if you wanted to study business you would have gone to MBA school! But, if you want to make your massage career all it can be and at the same time flourish financially, please read on for some business basics specifically tailored to massage therapy.

### Business Structures

If you're in private practice or an independent contractor you will need to choose the business structure that best suits you.

The vast majority of self-employed individual massage therapists choose to operate as Sole Proprietors. This business structure is by far the least complicated and most cost-effective way to go. You may file as a Sole Proprietor in your own name or in the name of your business if it is different than your own. For example, the name of my first private practice was called Soulstice Massage & Bodywork. It was just me back then, so I could file as an individual Sole Proprietor under my own business name. When you function as this type of business structure there is no difference between you and your business; they are one and the same.

Other options are limited liability partnerships, or corporations such as S, C or LLCs. When your business operates as one of these entities it is its own being, separate from you. If you have other partners involved or extenuating circumstances you may wish to investigate the suitability of these structures with your lawyer, accountant or tax preparer. There are significant costs and ongoing paperwork associated with establishing and operating as a corporation, so it is important to seek professional advice and carefully review the pros and cons. There may be some substantial advantages to incorporation, depending on your situation, so take some time to explore your options.

### Establishing a Business Bank Account

I recommend choosing a bank based on the following three key factors:

**Fees** – A bank should offer you a fee-free business checking account and advantageous features. Do some comparison shopping! Beware of "free" checking accounts which then gouge you for expensive checks and incidentals. Occasionally you will encounter an offer of "free" business checking, but then be charged excessively for the actual checks, ledgers, stamps and associated supplies. Obtain a written list of account features from a bank representative and ask for full disclosure on fees and penalties.

Inquire about overdraft charges, "stop payment" fees, bounced check fees (this one is *very* important to know if you plan on accepting checks from your clients), the cost to re-order checks, and any costs associated with online banking.

**Convenience** – Your bank should be well-located and convenient to your practice. Ideally, you don't want to have to travel across town every time you deposit a client's check. If you plan to use the convenience of online banking, ascertain if the bank charges any fees for paying bills or receiving payments via that medium. Ask the bank if you will receive paper statements in the mail or by email; monthly bank statements can be very helpful when it comes to keeping track of your income and expenses.

**Relationships** – Ideally you want to forge an ongoing relationship with your bankers and over time build a strong familiarity and rapport with them. Then, if one day you decide to expand, open a second office or need working capital, you will have some basis and track record for asking your bank for a small business loan or line of credit.

Remember the old adage, 'Don't mix business with pleasure?' In this context, anyway, it definitely does hold true! Once your business account is set up, keep it entirely separate from your personal banking accounts. Use your business checking account or business credit card to pay for all business-related expenses, never for personal. It makes life *much* easier for you and your accountant at tax time to have these accounts kept separate. Plus you will be able to keep track of your true business income that much more clearly if you put it all straight into its own account.

Whether banking-related or not, when entering into any kind of deal, signing up for services or establishing any kind of partnership, get everything down in writing. As much as you adore the person you're dealing with, get it in writing! Even if you can't ever imagine a time when you might regret it, get it in writing! You and your partner are best friends? Still, get it in writing!

When entering into any kind of agreement, be sure to request and check references. It may seem like a waste of time to ring strangers up to check references, but it is time immensely well spent. Ask your potential bankers or partners if you can speak to a few other businesses that have been using their services for some time. Individuals and company representatives can initially present themselves very differently than they actually are in reality. Believe me, you will save yourself much time and energy in the long run if you get all contracts and partnerships in writing. I'm a very trusting person, and historically optimistic to the point of idiocy at times, so take the word of someone who has learned this lesson the hard way. Protect yourself and your business at all times.

## Credit Cards & Merchant Accounts

Accepting credit cards is a wonderful convenience for your clients, enhances your professional image, and may boost your clientele. By accepting credit cards and *not* accepting checks you can also avoid paying bank fees that arise when clients bounce checks.

There are many companies out there who offer credit card processing services, some of better repute than others. In some states, once you file a declaration of business or fictitious business (DBA) statement it becomes a matter of public record and you may suddenly be inundated with merchant companies calling on you to pitch their services. Be ready for them!

When dealing with these companies, there are a few common pitfalls you should try to avoid. For instance, some merchant companies will tell you that you need to lease a credit card processor in order to swipe the credit card during transactions. Refuse to sign any kind of contract that requires you to lease or buy an expensive machine until you can have a lawyer look over it. Sometimes this lease is binding, and even if your merchant account may be cancelled, you can still get stuck with an unusable credit card machine and thousands of dollars in payments. Be sure to read the fine print on the contract and have your lawyer look it over.

Fees vary for each merchant processor, and it can get pretty complicated in sorting out who charges what. Simplify it by figuring out how many transactions you will process (based on how many sessions you expect to do in a month) and work with the sales rep to figure out which is the best plan for you. For example, merchants who process thousands of small ticket items per month should be on a different plan than you.

You will need to decide which credit cards you will accept, such as Visa, MasterCard, Discover, and American Express. Visa and MasterCard are commonly accepted together, but you will need to set up a merchant account directly with American Express to accept their cards. American Express charges a different fee structure and is often slightly more expensive for the merchant, but I found that given the choice a lot of my clients prefer to use their American Express cards. So, it's been worth it for me to accept those cards, too; you may find this to be true for your clients, or not.

Some clients may wish to pay using PayPal (www.paypal.com), a very easy-to-use online system that allows payments to be processed safely, securely and entirely over the internet. This method of payment is wonderful for prepaid packages, gift certificate purchases, and busy clients who don't have time to call with a credit card number. You can register for a free business account with PayPal that allows you to pay bills, receive payments and send invoices to clients via email. PayPal derives revenue much like the credit card companies; they take a small fee or percentage of each payment processed.

## Insurance Billing

Some states within the U.S. and foreign countries include massage therapy under the umbrella of standard, accepted health care practices thereby making it possible to bill insurance for your clients. Other states make the process complicated, costly, time-consuming and nearly impossible to get reimbursed within a reasonable amount of time.

If you are lucky enough to live in a place that makes insurance billing possible and relatively straightforward, these cases can be a strong source of steady income for your practice. It can open you up to referrals from chiropractors, physical therapists, orthopedists and a number of other health care professionals. There may be a learning curve at the beginning, but once you get the system down and optimized, insurance billing can be a great addition for both you and your client base.

It goes without saying that clients appreciate the option of having massage therapy covered by their health insurance, but it will be a highly individual decision as to whether it is worth your time and effort to offer this service in your practice. At a minimum, if a client believes their insurance may cover massage, I recommend offering them a super-bill. A super-bill is a detailed form containing the treatment a client is receiving, specific presenting complaints (sore back, etc.) and medical codes as necessary. Give the super-bill, along with a receipt for services, to your client. Then, they submit it all to their insurance company themselves. Let clients know on their initial intake form that while payment is due for their massage at the time services are provided, you are able to provide a super-bill for them upon request that they may submit and possibly receive reimbursement.

## Taxes and Deductions

This may seem like a no-brainer, but I've come across way too many massage therapists slapped with an audit or back taxes plus penalties for not paying their taxes properly. Don't let this be you!

Remember to pay your quarterly and yearly taxes on time and correctly. When it comes to taxes, a tax preparer that is familiar working with self-employed people, especially other massage therapists, can really pay off.

> *Don't forget that your tips are taxable income – if your employer keeps track of them, so should you!

Long before you open the doors to your independent massage therapy practice, prepare yourself to become the King or Queen of Receipts. Save receipts for absolutely everything you think you may be able to deduct; better to have it and throw it away than to wish you had saved something later.

When you are self-employed, you are responsible for paying self-employment taxes in addition to the taxes on all your income, including tips. You will be expected to make quarterly tax payments four times per year based on your projected income for that year. Be sure to make these payments on time to avoid potential penalties as well as reduce your tax liability at the end of the year.

Deductions are expenses that you may subtract from your income, lowering your overall tax basis and hence, your taxes. This applies to you whether you are an independent contractor, individual filer or a sole proprietor. If you plan to work for someone else or at a spa, be sure to ask your manager whether you will be an employee or a contractor when you are applying.

Some of the expenses you may be able to deduct are:
(Hint: Save these receipts!)

*Home office expense*
If you work from home, a percentage of your mortgage or rent may be
deductible. The amount you may deduct will be based on the square
footage of the space you use exclusively for your massage practice. In
recent years the IRS has been auditing a higher percentage of individuals
claiming a home office deduction, so be sure to carefully review this
expense with your accountant before claiming it.

*Massage table and supplies*
These include those expenses directly used in your massage practice
such as oils, lotions, linens, sheets, blankets, towels, massage tools,
essential oils, pillows and bolsters. When buying supplies, be sure to
check the retailer's return policy and manufacturer warranties especially
when you're dealing with big ticket items and those you will use for a
long time.

*Books and subscriptions*
You may deduct magazine subscriptions that are related to your massage
practice or provided for your clientele. Books on massage therapy,
business, anatomy and more may also be deductible expenses.

*Website and related expenses*
This may include your hosting service, internet connection (dial-up,
cable or broadband) and email service.

*Computer, printer, software*

*Work telephone*

*Training, education and workshops*

*Liability insurance*

*Business and general liability insurance*

*Health insurance*
Self-employed people may occasionally be able to deduct some of their
health insurance premiums as well as some medical expenses.

*Postage for client mailings*

*Office supplies*

*Paper, pens, paper clips, etc.*

*Water*

*Electricity*

*Garbage*

*Cleaning / Janitorial*

*Advertising*
This might include flyers, business cards, email marketing programs, print advertising and related design costs.

*Meals & Entertainment*

*Business License, if required*

*City / County Permits, if required*

*Automobile expenses*
These may include car payments, auto insurance, gasoline, services, oil changes and repairs if you use your automobile regularly as part of your work. This is especially applicable for therapists with a primarily outcall business.

*Parking and Tolls*

*Linens & Laundry*
If you are working as an employee, your linens and laundry will generally be taken care of by your employer. But if you are an independent contractor or running your own office, it pays to do some research on your options for linens and laundry.

*Charitable donations*

# CHAPTER 17

## PLANNING FOR YOUR FUTURE

### Taking Care of Your Body and Mind

A career in massage therapy and healing work can provide you with a long term, enriching profession and independent lifestyle. However, performing massage is directly dependent on your physical health and maintaining your strength and energy. Therefore, it is imperative that you take especially good care of your body and mind. At the outset of your practice and throughout your career, build self-care practices into your daily routine. The more consistently you exercise, stretch, meditate and receive bodywork, the more readily these actions will become healthy habits.

### Grow and Diversify

Many therapists, having established a strong foundation in massage, choose to branch out into other healing modalities. You may wish to acquire new skills that are not dependent on your physical body, so in the event you injure yourself or need to cut back on your massage practice, you can still support yourself in a helping profession. Some avenues you may want to explore are counseling, coaching, talk therapies, hypnotherapy, energy work modalities, acupuncture, chiropractic and physical therapy. Other therapists move into complementary work, such as nutrition and supplement sales, spa management, teaching, writing, consulting or massage-related retail employment.

It is important to recognize that massage therapy is a very 'giving' profession, and to take conscious steps to maintain physical and emotional balance in your life. In other words, you will need to nourish yourself and bring in the love and compassion you give out to your clients on a regular basis. Balancing your massage business with other activities and interests will make you a more rounded practitioner and better able to practice massage for many years to come.

## Plan and Invest

Once you have developed and built a private practice or independent massage career, whether you realize it or not, you are now an entrepreneur and business owner. Being in business over the course of many years means negotiating ups and downs and navigating through extreme highs and lows. You will be dealing with a level of responsibility you may not have experienced before, and planning is crucial.

Investing for the future is an integral part of planning, especially in a career that is dependent upon your ongoing health and physical body. Running your own business and practice is very different than working a salaried job or receiving a steady paycheck from a company. In most cases, you will need to plan and invest in your own health care insurance and retirement account. Get professional help from knowledgeable financial advisors and establish a long-term savings plan that best suits your needs. Make provisions for the possibility of an unexpected break from massage work due to illness or injury. Determine a temporary back-up plan you can enact quickly if necessary.

In closing, I would like to pass on some of the more valuable business advice I have received over the years.

- Remember to breathe.
- Don't make decisions when you are emotional. Give yourself space and time, and then revisit and deal with the issue.
- Maintain a long view and perspective – don't sweat the small stuff!
- Laugh. Especially at yourself.
- Don't be afraid to ask for what you want in life.
- Stay positive, yet realistic. Keep your head in the clouds but your feet on the ground.
- Always keep in mind there will be situations and developments that are out of our control. When these events occur, sometimes we can only control our reactions to them. Even when things don't work out the way we want them to, responding with honest words and honorable actions will be remembered long after our mistakes or failures.

Massage therapy is an amazing career, promising meaningful work, deep connections and constant growth and learning. I hope this book provides you with some measure of assistance, camaraderie, reassurance and guidance, whether you are merely curious about massage or are a long-time therapist in need of a little spark. I wish you a successful, joyful and fulfilling journey throughout your massage therapy career.

# GLOSSARY OF TERMS

Acupressure: A Traditional Chinese Medicine (TCM) form of healing that employs the hands, fingers, elbows or forearms to apply pressure along the body's pressure points and meridians

Acupuncture: A healing system that involves the insertion and manipulation of very fine needles to specific points and meridians on the body. It is widely associated with Traditional Chinese Medicine and practiced throughout Asia.

Ayurveda: An ancient Indian healing system that incorporates massage along with diet and herbs for health and healing

CranioSacral: A gentle form of bodywork that manipulates and realigns the craniosacral system, including the spine, neck, sacrum and cranial bones

Draping: Mindfully covering a client with sheets, towels and/or blankets to keep them warm and contribute to their feeling of safety and privacy

Eastern Massage: Bodywork modalities with Eastern origins, such as Thai, Shiatsu, Chi Nei Tsang, Ayurveda, Jin Shin Jyutsu and Acupressure

Effleurage: Light, sweeping, integrative massage strokes performed with a flat hand; excellent for warming up the tissues when beginning a massage as well as integrating different parts of the body throughout the treatment

Energy Work: Healing modalities that focus on balancing and restoring the client's energy; they can be performed with a very light touch, within the body's aura, in the energy field exterior to the physical body, or at a distance

Fascia: Connective tissue that surrounds and contains the muscles and organs

Face Cradle: Also known as a head rest, it is the part of a massage table—usually removable and adjustable—that the client rests their head in when face down on the massage table

Friction: A type of massage stroke characterized by a back-and-forth rubbing of the skin to create warmth and generate circulation in the tissue

Meridians: Energetic pathways in the body

Modalities: Different types or styles of massage

Petrissage: A type of massage stroke similar to kneading

Polarity: A type of energy work that emphasizes balancing the body's energy

Qigong: Traditional movement and breathing exercises that assist in the accumulation, circulation and optimization of qi (chi), or energy within the body

Reiki: An ancient, very gentle form of energy work of Japanese or Tibetan origin

Rolfing: Named after its founder, Ida Rolf, a deep, structural style of bodywork that realigns the body's musculature

Tapotement: A type of massage stroke characterized by rhythmic tapping and percussion

Traditional Chinese Medicine (TCM): Typically known as Chinese or alternative medicine in the United States, TCM incorporates bodywork, herbal medicine, acupuncture, and exercise in its health care system

Trigger Points: Compacted, tender spots on the body that respond well to deep, sustained pressure along specific points, ideally resulting in a muscle adhesion's unwinding and release

Vibration: A type of massage stroke characterized by repetitive, quickly-applied movements and pressure intended to create warmth in the musculature and loosen adhesions

Breinigsville, PA USA
05 May 2010
237418BV00003B/64/P